FRANÇOIS MATTHES

AND THE MARKS OF TIME

Middle Cathedral Rock, Yosemite. By Ansel Adams

FRANÇOIS MATTHES
AND THE MARKS OF TIME

Yosemite and the High Sierra

EDITED BY FRITIOF FRYXELL

SIERRA CLUB » SAN FRANCISCO

The Sierra Club, founded in 1892 by John Muir, has devoted itself to the study
and protection of national scenic resources, particularly those of mountain regions.
All Sierra Club publications are part of the nonprofit publishing effort
the Club carries on as a public trust. Participation is invited in the program
to enjoy and preserve wilderness, wildlife, forests, and streams.
Address: Mills Tower, San Francisco 4.

DEDICATED TO
EDITH LOVELL MATTHES

PREFACE

FRANÇOIS MATTHES, said Robert Gordon Sproul, President of the University of California, "interpreted the beauty of the Western American Landscape to the mind as well as eyes of all who love the mountains."

Dr. Sproul spoke for many: those who could testify that Matthes had made them more than just spectators of land forms, by giving them a fresh and deeper insight into the meaning of what they saw, so that, under his tutelage, intelligent understanding was added to their initial admiration and wonder.

As an interpreter of the western scene, Matthes was without peer among contemporary American geologists. Even when writing technical papers he kept in mind the interested laymen who shared his interests. Recently a Sierra Club leader wrote me, with reference to a friend and himself (neither of them geologists), "We have both carried Professional Paper 160 in our knapsacks when every ounce of weight was precious." This tribute would have meant much to Matthes. His concern with the general public netted him little in terms of professional standing, but this did not deter him from giving unstintingly of his time and effort to such "extracurricular" activities. The latter were important, he knew, because they enriched the lives of others. This was sufficient.

Matthes' eagerness to impart to others what he himself perceived in landscapes led him, very early in his career, to contribute geological essays to mountaineering and other journals. Some of his finest essays were written about the National Parks—Mount Rainier, Yosemite, Grand Canyon, and Crater Lake—and were printed on the reverse side of the topographic maps of these areas. This use assured them exceptionally wide distribution, and it put them in the hands of those most likely to read them with profit and appreciation. The literary charm of these essays, coupled with their high level of scientific reliability, made them—and continues to make them—uniquely effective in the interpretative program of the National Park Service. Most of Matthes' essays, however, were written for the *Bulletin* of the Sierra Club, and were addressed primarily to his fellow members in that group.

The present volume brings together fifteen representative essays written between 1911 and 1938. This twenty-seven year period spans only a part of the time which Matthes devoted to Sierra studies, as that time extended, with only a few interruptions, from 1905 until his death in 1948. The choice of essays was made with a view to achieving unity in the collection (all of the essays relate to the Sierra Nevada, and all have general appeal as regards subject matter and treatment) while also illustrating the diversity to be found in the descriptive and expository writings of this author. Five of the essays are here published for the first time.

It is possible that when Matthes began writing his Sierra essays he contemplated a series, dealing mainly with the Yosemite, which eventually might be assembled in book form. At any rate, between 1910 and 1914 he wrote five essays for the *Sierra Club Bulletin* all entitled "Little Studies in the Yosemite Valley," each with an appropriate subtitle and numbered, consecutively, I to V. His next Sierra essay did not appear until 1920, and it was entitled simply "Cockscomb Crest." The six year gap in the series resulted, at least in part, from World War I, but abandonment of the general title and plan for numbering may be attributed to other circumstances. Most of the essays written after 1920 were hardly "Little Studies," as were the earlier ones, nor did they relate only to the Yosemite region. (Publication of Professional Paper 160, *Geologic History of Yosemite Valley,* in 1930 provided adequately for Matthes' Yosemite studies.) Rather, they dealt with many and widely scattered geomorphic features in the Sierra Nevada, and they reflected the vastly broadened sweep of his interests, which by this time encompassed some of the most fundamental problems of the Sierra as a whole.

Some repetition will be found in this book—necessarily so—overlapping being inescapable since each essay was written to be a unit complete in itself. However, the amount of repetition is relatively small, and if the essays are read individually, as will generally be the case, it should not prove disturbing. The essays have been arranged chronologically for the most part, a few have been shortened slightly, and editorial annotations (signed "Ed." to distinguish them from the author's own footnotes) have been kept to a minimum. In some instances, recent photographs have been substituted for the original photographs which now seem archaic—for photography and the techniques of reproducing photographic illustrations have come a long way since the early volumes of the *Sierra Club Bulletin* were printed. Features mentioned in these essays are shown on the topographic maps of Yosemite Valley and Yosemite National Park,

Sequoia and Kings Canyon National Parks, and the Mount Lyell, Mount Morrison, Mount Goddard, and Kaiser quadrangles. Elevations used in the book come from editions of these U.S. Geological Survey topographic maps (scale 1:125,000) which preceded the more accurate, photogrammetrically based maps now being issued (scale 1:62,500). There were minor interim adjustments of elevations in the course of the study period represented in the Matthes essays; no attempt has been made to correct the essays accordingly.

Readers wishing to go farther afield with Matthes, through the medium of other essays and more technical papers, may consult the Selected Bibliography referred to on page 39 for specific suggestions. In particular they may wish to seek acquaintance with the monograph already alluded to, Professional Paper 160, and two posthumous books, *The Incomparable Valley: a geologic interpretation of the Yosemite,* and *Sequoia National Park: a geological album,* published in 1950 by the University of California Press. Mention may be made of another posthumous work, Professional Paper 329, *Reconnaissance of the Geomorphology and Glacial Geology of the San Joaquin Basin, Sierra Nevada, California,* published in 1960.

This volume, like its predecessors, *The Incomparable Valley* and *Sequoia National Park,* embodies the vision and planning of August Frugé and David Brower of the Sierra Club. Encouraged by these friends, I undertook to prepare the book in the summer of 1953, as a joint venture with my oldest son, John, then 22, who gladly did the essential preliminary copying of the essays, checked the typescript against the original texts, and critically reviewed my first draft of the biographical account. With John's death that fall, the work ceased. Later I returned to the project and this time, with the help of my other sons, Roald and Redwood, completed it. Carol Broline and Lois Wittbecker also aided me, with the retyping of parts of the final manuscript and Mona Goranson assisted with proofreading.

Ansel Adams, with typical generosity, allowed the Sierra Club to explore his files of Sierra photographs and donated all that would be particularly appropriate to the book. Special thanks are also due George Mauger, of the Sequoia and Kings Canyon National Parks Company, for photographs in the Tokopah Valley chapter. All of the François Matthes photographs are used here by permission of the U.S. Geological Survey. Other illustrations were originally published in early *Sierra Club Bulletins* or have been taken from the club's photographic collection. Robert V. Golden, of the club's staff, aided in their selection and identification. Mark Robertson, the book's designer, contributed above and beyond the call of duty in his concern about content as well as form. Professor William Putnam, at the University of California, Los Angeles, encouraged the final effort to bring the book into print, and Bruce M. Kilgore, as Managing Editor for the Sierra Club, staunchly carried it through its final stages at a time when conservation crises were making extraordinary demands.

Readers will share the gratitude I feel to those who helped, in these various ways, to give this selection of "Matthes gem-like essays" a place among the admirable books bearing the distinguished imprint of the Sierra Club.

F. F.

Rock Island, Illinois
November 30, 1961

CONTENTS

François E. Matthes

FRANÇOIS EMILE MATTHES

RANÇOIS EMILE and Gerard Henrik Matthes, twin brothers, were born
in Amsterdam, Holland, March 16, 1874. Their parents both belonged to old,
distinguished families of the Netherlands.

Willem Ernst Matthes, the father, was a well-to-do merchant, member of
the firm of Matthes and Bormeester, dealers in colonial products such as rubber,
indigo, and hemp, the firm that had the contract to furnish India rubber for the
first transatlantic cable, laid in 1866. He had traveled widely throughout Europe
and was a man of broad culture and many interests. He was the founder and
first president of an academy of arts and sciences, known as "Felix Meritis,"
which was inaugurated by William III of Orange, King of Holland; and he was
also a director of the "Natura Artis Magistra," the famous Amsterdam Zoologi-
cal Gardens. Fond of horseback riding, he owned several saddle horses, was one
of the organizers of the riding academy of Amsterdam, and, as a Lieutenant
Colonel in the National Guard, commanded the artillery unit of Amsterdam.

The mother, Jonkvrouw Johanna Suzanna Matthes, née van der Does de
Bije, was a delicate but singularly beautiful and refined woman, with a keen
mind and a flair for history. She was the youngest of thirteen children, six
brothers and seven sisters, who were brought up in the old university town of
Leiden, and mingled in court circles at the Hague. The clan, van der Does, to
which she belonged, was of the nobility of Holland and well deserved the sur-
name of "de Bije" (the bees). Johanna—Nancy as she was usually called—
was a lineal descendant of Janus van der Does, the patriot Commandant of the
City of Leiden in its epic resistance to the Spaniards in the siege of 1574.

The Matthes home, on the Heeren Gracht near the corner of Vijzel Straat,
was a stately mansion facing one of Amsterdam's canals. It was the center of
numerous social affairs, dazzling with decorations, uniforms, and sabers. The
little twins could peek at all this splendor but themselves had no part in it.
However, life-size marble busts of the boys, made when they were five, graced
the banquet hall of the home.

13

Gerard vividly remembers the vacations which the family spent at Trouville and Biarritz, France. At Biarritz, where the ocean tides were dangerously high, the shore was lined with sheer cliffs, and the beach was strewn with boulders. The twins, then eight, discovered that these boulders contained fossils, and they proceeded to chisel them out with little hammers. Their collection became so big (and heavy) that, at time of departure, the mother refused to pack it in their

Willem Ernst Matthes

François Emile Matthes at age six

trunks, and dumped it all out, to their great dismay. Perhaps this early venture in fossil collecting should be regarded as prophetic of the geologic interests which both boys manifested later, in mature years. At Biarritz, Willem Matthes engaged a two-horse landau and a driver, and took his family on trips into the Pyrenees and the country of the Basques, and even down the coast to Irun, in Spain.

When about eight years of age, the twins began to be troubled with malaria. The disease was common in Amsterdam, but since its cause was not understood no measures were taken to check the breeding of mosquitoes in the canals. The family doctor, Van Wezel, an able man for his time, recommended for the boys a sojourn of several years in the Alps, which were known to be malaria-free. Accordingly, when the twins were nearly ten, it was decided that the mother should take them to Switzerland, there to lay the foundations of health and cosmopolitan education,—a decision which, Gerard affirms, was a turning point in their lives. As a result of it, François, though born below the level of the sea, became a lover of the mountains and gave most of his life to their study.

Gerard and François, with their mother,
about 1886

At Courgevaux, a few miles from Lac Morat, the mother found a school suitable for foreigners, and they took residence near by in a wing of the castle of the Count of Pourtal, who was away. It was an enchanting abode, set amidst immaculate, spacious gardens; and the twins thoroughly enjoyed their mile-long walk from the castle to school. In Lac Morat they could see rows of stumps, remnants of the piles which in ancient times supported the homes of the Lake Dwellers. Wading in the lake they found relics of the army of Charles *le Temeraire* (last Duke of Burgundy), which at this spot was overwhelmed by

15

the Swiss in 1476. From the nearest town, Murten, the boys could hike to the ruins of a Roman amphitheater.

Gerard recalls,

We lived in the castle more than a year. The pupils at school were of all ages and spoke many languages. There were English, Germans, Americans, Italians, a Spaniard, a Greek, and an Egyptian prince, and other nationalities. The young boys were placed under the supervision of the more mature ones; our mentor was a bright young Englishman. He taught us boxing, running races, and playing cricket. We learned to speak French fluently, and picked up a smattering of German (spoken throughout Switzerland) and some English words.

In 1885–1886, when we were eleven, we lived first at Montreux in a first-class hotel overlooking Lake Geneva, and later in a smaller hotel called "Montfleuri," perched on the steep mountain side and affording gorgeous views of the lake and the snow-capped mountains to the southeast, the Dent-du-Midi. Life at Montfleuri, too, was a joy to us boys. We fell to sketching Lake Geneva, the steamers on it, and the Dent-du-Midi. We learned swimming in the lake near the picturesque Castle of Chillon.

Living half-way up the mountain meant going down to lake level to attend a private school at Territet, where the pupils were mostly English boys. This called for a daily mountaineering stunt. I attribute our capacity for climbing mountains later in life to our excellent lung capacity developed by this daily exercise. We learned to run uphill when chasing butterflies, and climbed to high altitudes to collect rare species. We studied the ways of different kinds of ants.

Father spent a week or two with us each summer. His hobby was mountaineering, and we enjoyed it with him. At Montfleuri our favorite climb was to the top of the nearby Dent de Jaman, 5000 feet above lake level. Father brought us cloth-mounted military maps (General Dufour's series) which showed all triangulation stations. On the ground these stations were marked by tall white timber pyramids. The maps had no contours, but were beautifully finished with hatchures, which brought out the relief in great detail. Father taught us to read the maps and we learned to locate ourselves. After he left we always carried the maps in our blouses, and roamed about without fear of getting lost.

Becoming "map wise" as boys was to prove of tremendous help to the twins in later years.

Vacations were spent at various alpine resorts. One of these was noted for its fine St. Bernard dogs, and on their expeditions the boys always took one or two of the dogs along. On their final trip to a resort in the Alps, they crossed the border to celebrated Chamonix, in France. Here they visited the great glaciers of Mont Blanc. Standing upon *Le Glacier des Bossons*, they marveled at the intense blue green of the ice deep down in its crevasses.

Little wonder that, after four years of such idyllic boyhood, frail bodies became strong; bright, inquiring minds were stimulated; and as the twigs were bent the trees inclined.

Themselves patrons and collectors of art, the parents saw to it that from the age of nine on the twins received instruction in drawing with pencil, charcoal, and drawing inks. François revealed a native talent for art which amazed everyone. The boy was fascinated by the work of the American artist, Frederick Remington, which he studied until he, too, became adept at drawing animals, particularly horses. François' boyhood sketch books have been preserved, and leafing through their pages, crowded with exquisitely drawn horses, in every imaginable pace and attitude, one cannot but wonder whether, had he pursued the career of an artist, he might not have rivaled Remington, or the noted French contemporary painter of animals, Rosa Bonheur. However, the education of the Matthes twins had been planned along quite different lines, as is evident from the fact that, beginning also at the age of nine, they were taught to draw on tracing linen, with use of triangles, T-square, and drawing pens.

In 1887 the twins, now thirteen, procured German grammars and began serious study of the German language. That fall their mother brought them to Frankfurt am Main, in Germany. Here they were left in care of one Professor Goedeke, and in his home shared quarters with four other school boys. Their studies were now continued at the Klingerschule, a technical high school ("Ober-realschule"). Besides German, they received excellent instruction in both French and English, —in accordance with Willem Matthes' wish that his sons "learn 'live' languages thoroughly and skip Latin and Greek." Gymnastics and out-of-doors sports were also taught, including swimming, in the River Main.

Refreshing changes from school life were provided by the summer months, when they visited their home in Amsterdam; traveled through France, Germany, and Switzerland; or stayed at Villa Favorita, the summer residence of the family at Baarn (near the beaches and dunes of Holland), or visited at Chateau Einthout, near Brussels, Belgium, the country estate of the Baroness van der Elst, a great friend of the Matthes family for whose deceased husband François Emile had been named. On their trips between Amsterdam and Frankfurt, the boys traveled by train along the Rhine, going down one side and back along the other, so as not to miss any of the fine scenery.

The studies at Frankfurt were intended as preparation for an engineering course at a German university; but after the twins had spent four years in Germany, their plans underwent another momentous change, when fate intervened—in the person of a traveling Harvard professor—and instead, in September 1891 they set out on a long voyage, to *Amerika*. At the outset of the voyage, a violent storm disabled their ship, so that the adventure all but ended in disaster, but eventually, though days behind schedule, they reached New York harbor. When they sought admission to the Massachusetts Institute of Technology, the semester was already under way, but the president, General Francis A. Walker, becoming interested in the twins, permitted them to take the entrance examinations. These showed them to be far ahead of requirements in modern language and mathematics, and deficient only in American History. They were admitted at once to the civil engineering course, as freshmen, but were excused from taking French and (being foreigners) from military drill.

Thus, in all the strangeness of a foreign land the twins began life anew and in their fourth language, English. With the writing of English they had little difficulty, as they were actually better prepared than most of their American classmates, so thorough had been their instruction at the Ober-realschule; and their rapid progress in the mastery of spoken English is evidenced by the fact that they were soon giving talks to the Civil Engineering Society of the Institute and other groups, on various technical subjects. Some of these subjects, though very familiar to them, must have been novel to their fellow students. François, for instance, spoke on "The Draining of the Zuider Zee" and "The Use of Mattresses in Dike Construction." Their early training in drawing and drafting now stood them in good stead; François soon became the outstanding draftsman in his class. At the advice of a professor who had formerly been connected with the U. S. Coast and Geodetic Survey, the boys elected the geodetic course, which would prepare them for careers with that Survey.

Both boys became active members of the Agassiz Association of Boston; Gerard, as a senior, was elected president of the society. Their large insect collection from Switzerland they presented to the Museum of Natural History in Boston and, in return, were allowed free use of the museum library. Their interest in entomology continued. François, in autobiographical notes from the period, refers to illustrated talks which he gave to the Agassiz Association and other groups in Boston and elsewhere on "Coleoptera"; "Parasitic Insects"; "Insect Life in Winter", and other entomological topics.

Their first summer in the United States, 1892, the boys pursued their favorite pastimes—camping, mountaineering, and collecting insects—in the White Mountains. The second summer they were employed by an insurance company to make drawings of the fire-protection devices used in various eastern factories. With their earnings they paid their way to Chicago, to see that city's first World Fair. The third summer, spent at the M.I.T. field school in the Adirondacks, they learned mapping with plane table and alidade, and, in the Ausable River, measuring stream flow with different kinds of current meters.

General Walker proved their constant warm friend and counselor; Gerard reciprocated by writing the "Military Career of General Walker" (in the Civil War) for the college annual. The busy college years sped swiftly and happily by. In 1895 the twins both graduated with honors, receiving the degree Bachelor of Science, and the next year they proudly became citizens of the United States.

At this point we must separate the twins, Gerard and François. Each went his way to climb to the top of his profession. Gerard distinguished himself in the field of hydrographic engineering (see *Who's Who in America* and *American Men of Science*); François for many years expressed his talent for drawing, as well as for precise, analytical scientific work, in the making of topographic maps. Eventually, however, he became a geomorphologist and a glacial geologist. As the latter specialty came to include the study of existing glaciers it, in turn, led him far into the related fields of meteorology and climatology.

Following graduation, on June 1, 1895, François entered upon the duties of his first position, which was as instrument man and draftsman in the city engineer's office at Rutland, Vermont, and was assigned to the making of detailed topographic surveys for the city. Exactly one year later he joined the organization with which he was to be connected for fifty-one years: the United States Geological Survey. From June 1 to November 1, 1896, he was traverseman with topographic parties in New York and Vermont. He then became field assistant in Indian Territory (now a section of Oklahoma), part of the time serving as acting chief draftsman, part of the time being in charge of revision work in the field. On April 1, 1898, having passed the federal Civil Service examination, he was advanced to assistant topographer, a grade which qualified him for the larger opportunities now at hand.

In the summer of 1898, the United States was at war with Spain, but pressing domestic projects were under way also. Little-known areas of the West were being mapped by the Geological Survey. Early in the summer, Matthes received his first assignment as a party chief, in connection with surveying the Cloud Peak quadrangle in Wyoming. The lower, western third of the quadrangle had been surveyed by H. S. Wallace in 1897; it remained for Matthes to survey the remainder of the quadrangle, including all the main crest of the Bighorn Mountains, in 1898 and 1899. From Washington he went west by train, arriving, on July 20, 1898, at the frontier town of Sheridan, where he proceeded to organize the personnel and equipment of his party. It was no task for a weakling, either with respect to the exploration of these trackless mountains or the problems involved in the mapping; but the physical difficulties were, of course, simply part of the day's work. The map was the thing!

Of Matthes' work as topographer, it has been said that he "contributed notably to the effectiveness of mapping rugged mountain areas," and that this method, which involved multiple sights through the telescopic alidade and the sketching of provisional form lines, has become standard procedure (Visher). (Prior to about 1935, all the topographic maps produced by the Geological Survey were made with the use of the alidade and plane table.) Matthes' success as a topographer stemmed not only from mastery of technical principles and methods, and from his skill in drawing, but also from his keen analysis of land forms and his consuming desire to understand them. The Bighorn Mountains provided him with his first opportunity to delineate, with contour lines, the varied patterns of mountain landscapes, especially those resulting from alpine glaciation; and as he brought out the topographic features on his maps he pondered over their origin. Thus, following his field work, in 1899, he rendered a service beyond the call of duty as topographer when, in the evenings, after long days of drafting at the Washington office, he wrote *Glacial Sculpture of the Bighorn Mountains, Wyoming*. This was his first scientific publication, and it is still a standard reference. In it Matthes distinguished from the land forms sculptured by glaciers other features produced by persistent snow fields, and he applied the now-familiar term "nivation" to the previously unrecognized geomorphic processes which were involved.

From his initial assignment in the Rocky Mountains, Matthes emerged a seasoned topographer of recognized skill, and a first-rate horseman and packer, with experience which was to prove all but indispensable to him in his future work. On July 1, 1899, he was promoted to the rank of full topographer. In the spring of 1900 he made a hydrographic reconnaissance of the Blackfoot Indian Reservation in Montana. There followed a succession of assignments which included two areas in Montana (the Chief Mountain quadrangle and part of the adjacent Browning quadrangle, surveyed in the summers of 1900 and 1901), two areas in Arizona (the Bradshaw Mountains quadrangle, surveyed in the winter of 1900–1901, and the Jerome quadrangle, surveyed in the winter of 1902–1903), and several other areas which, from the standpoint of the topographer, were as difficult and spectacular, and therefore as challenging, as any to be found in the entire Far West.

Matthes, albeit sturdily built, was a man of rather small stature, and there was little in his appearance to suggest his capacity for enduring hardships and strenuous activity of the kind that these assignments necessitated. That he became a master of reconnaissance mapping—first topographic and later geologic, much of it carried out in exceedingly difficult terrain without benefit of roads, or, for that matter, even trails, at a time when modern aids to mapping such as aerial photography were unheard of—may be attributed not only to hardihood and perseverence but also to his consummate skill in planning and executing long pack trips, and to his great resourcefulness in solving the problems posed by exploration in wilderness country.

In the Chief Mountain quadrange, as in the Cloud Peak quadrangle, Matthes found glacial sculpturing illustrated on a grand scale and with remarkable clarity; and there was even better opportunity to study small but interesting existing glaciers. He established stations on a number of the principal summits and determined the elevations of the peaks. It became evident, as the map grew, that what had heretofore been "just Rocky Mountains," insofar as official Washington knew, was a veritable "Alps." Conservation was to the fore, enthusiasm grew, and the superb Chief Mountain quadrangle, together with Matthes' photographic records and his publications, gave telling impetus to the movement which culminated in 1910 in the act of Congress establishing Glacier National Park.

In February 1902 came orders to begin the mapping of the upper half of the Grand Canyon of the Colorado River, in Arizona, the scenically more remarkable section of the canyon which was destined later (1919) to become Grand Canyon

National Park. Aside from the difficulties of getting about in, and mapping, some 500 square miles of almost incredibly rugged country—country dissected with labryinthine complexity and traversed by a mile-deep chasm considered impassable—and of maintaining the life of men and animals in a forbidding, practically uninhabited region, largely devoid of usable water supply, the assignment was a staggering undertaking, the full details of which have yet to be told.[1] Suffice it to say that the mapping was done wholly by means of the plane table, the Grand Canyon providing, in Matthes' words, "an extreme test of the efficiency of that instrument." It was the original intention to publish the maps in 15-minute quadrangles, on the standard scale of 1:62,500 and with 100-foot contour intervals. However, preliminary experimentation convinced Matthes that while his field map, made on the scale of 1:48,000, with 50-foot contour intervals, best expressed the significant topographic elements, this map would not stand reduction to the standard scale. He therefore traced a detail of his field map (delineating Zoroaster Temple) and sent it to Washington, with the recommendation that the Grand Canyon quadrangle be made an exception to usual practice and be published on the scale of 1:48,000, with 50-foot contour intervals. The recommendation was approved. It followed that the field maps had to be drawn with such accuracy and neatness that they could serve, unreduced, as copy for the engraver. This necessitated the most painstaking kind of drafting, first in pencil and later in ink, but as a result the maps were published with the scale and contour interval best adapted to bringing out the distinctive topography of the Grand Canyon.

Matthes began the survey, the first summer, by crossing the canyon with his pack train to the north rim, and working on the high northern plateaus. As the mapping progressed, he studied out through his telescope the details of a remarkably long, straight side canyon, that of Bright Angel Creek, which he recognized as marking the trace of a fault, and along which the cliffs had disintegrated into loose talus. As winter approached, the men hastily built a trail down this talus, while Matthes himself worked from dawn to dark to finish the mapping before the heavy snows would set in. Early on November 9, with work on the Kaibab Plateau finally finished, they broke camp and descended the improvised trail into Bright Angel Canyon. The sky was ominous, and that night it rained at their camp. The next morning the Kaibab was white with snow.

[1] The account here given is summarized mainly from the paper by François E. Matthes and Richard T. Evans, Map of Grand Canyon National Park. *The Military Engineer,* volume 18, 1926, pages 188–201.

As Matthes noted succinctly, they had "left none too soon." The route which they then blazed through Bright Angel Canyon is, in all essential points, the one today followed by the Kaibab Trail, now the principal tourist route across the Grand Canyon (the spectacular inner gorge has been spanned by a steel suspension bridge). On November 16, when work in lower Bright Angel Canyon

U.S.G.S. Camp in El Capitan Meadow, Yosemite Valley, 1906

was completed, they recrossed the Colorado River by swimming their horses behind a boat found on the banks. Next day they climbed out of the Grand Canyon and made camp on the south rim. They were hailed as conquering heroes.[2]

The mapping of the Grand Canyon continued in 1903, and only on January

[2] History and exploration of the Grand Canyon Region: *Natural History Bulletin No. 2,* Grand Canyon Natural History Association, November, 1935, pages 18–22.

26, 1904, after nearly two years of practically continuous field work, did Matthes leave by train for Washington. There remained the task of inking the maps and supervising the engraving, eye-straining work which permanently impaired Matthes' sight. The end products of this labor, however, the Bright Angel and Vishnu quadrangles, stand as examples of topographic excellence which have never been surpassed. Many years later, in 1933, when the geologists participat-

Yosemite, 1906. F. C. North, F. E. Matthes, F. Austin, and L. V. Degnan

ing in an excursion of the Sixteenth International Geological Congress stopped at the Grand Canyon, the members of the group affixed their autographs to the back of a panoramic view of the canyon and sent it to Matthes with the message, "We have been using your maps and have marvelled at them. There are no other such topographic maps in all the world."

In June 1903 Matthes interrupted his work at the Grand Canyon to travel by train and stage coach to Yosemite National Park, California. The entry in his tiny diary on Sunday, June 14, reads, ". . . had front seats on stage coming into Valley. First view from Inspiration Point overwhelming." Though he had gone to Yosemite for a rest, his brief entries for the next four days—the entire

24

duration of his "vacation"—would seem to indicate that his object was not attained. Such a rushing about on foot from the Valley to Glacier Point and Sentinel Dome; to Vernal and Nevada Falls; to the brink of Yosemite Falls and back again to the valley! But of the fact that mind and body were refreshed we are left in not the slightest doubt. He had dreamed of Yosemite ever since coming to America. Now he had beheld it at the height of its springtime beauty, and he was never to forget.

In the winter of 1904–1905, Matthes took a postgraduate course in geology at Harvard University, majoring in geomorphology under Professor William Morris Davis. While at Harvard he also lectured on "topographic field methods for advanced students in geology," under an Austin Teaching Fellowship. The winter in Cambridge was profitable and stimulating at the University, while, on the outside, there was opportunity for some social life as well as for cultural diversions—lectures, the theater, and music—for which, by this time, he was fairly starving.

Matthes had almost fulfilled requirements for the M.S. degree when there came the offer from the Survey to make a large-scale (1:24,000) map of the Yosemite Valley. This was an opportunity he could not forego, but he inquired if he might not be allowed the few weeks of university work necessary for completion of his course. The reply was negative: the season for field work in the Sierra Nevada was short, and if he wished to undertake the assignment he must start at the earliest possible date. He hesitated no longer. There was but one Yosemite Valley. The chance to map it was worth far more than an additional degree. On June 14 he stood once more in the Yosemite Valley. Camp was set up on the valley floor that afternoon.

If the Grand Canyon had been intricate and involved, the Yosemite Valley was far more difficult to map, for, where the Canyon was all angles and points which were natural "targets" for the triangulator, the valley presented curves and even overhanging arches. Matthes worked out his own system of expressing these features in contour lines, and as he worked his wonder grew that such a diversity of rock forms could be found in so small an area, and that side valleys could hang at such great and varied heights above the main stream. What factors were these that had contrived to produce so amazing a spectacle?

Two seasons were necessary to complete the field work on the Yosemite map. On October 30, 1906, Matthes began inking the map at the Sacramento office of the Survey, and, with the beautiful work of the engravers at Washington completed, in July of 1907 the "Yosemite Special" was an accomplished fact.

25

In 1923 Matthes wrote an interpretative text for the reverse side of this map—one of a number of such essays which, at various times, he wrote for the maps of National Parks and other areas, and which have been greatly appreciated by the general public.

Matthes spent the spring of 1906 at Berkeley, California, assisting Grove Karl Gilbert in a study of the transportation of sediment by rivers, aiding both with the laboratory experiments and by reviewing the extensive Dutch literature relating to silt deposition in the rivers of Holland.

On April 18 occurred the great San Francisco earthquake. Thus it chanced that Gilbert and Matthes were among those who, from the Berkeley Hills, witnessed the conflagration which in the following days spread further disaster through the city across the bay. The earthquake provided more than an unforeseen interruption of their scheduled work. Gilbert was appointed to the California State Earthquake Investigating Commission, and Matthes, assigned to the field almost immediately on behalf of this Commission, traced out and mapped the San Andreas Rift through the northern half of the State. He also made a special detailed map of the rift in the vicinity of Fort Ross, in Sonoma County. His maps were published in the atlas prepared by the Commission, and his field observations, relating particularly to the rift as a geomorphic feature, were embodied in the Commission's two-volume report.

From 1907 to 1913, Matthes served as an Inspector of Maps for the Geological Survey. The several Inspectors visited their widely scattered field parties during the summer months; in winter, at Washington, they supervised the work of the topographers, as the latter completed the drafting and inking of their field manuscripts. In January 1908 Matthes and four associates founded the Quadrangle Club, for senior topographers; the same month the junior topographers likewise organized, forming the Triangle Club. Richard T. Evans, veteran topographer, recalls that in the winter of 1907–1908 were held the first of the many meetings—frequently three or four a month—sponsored by the Topographic Branch as a whole, or by these clubs, for purposes of instruction, and for the exchange of experiences and views. These meetings (some held at the Cosmos Club) were continued until 1917, when the ranks of the topographers at Washington became depleted during the War.

Matthes was a leading spirit in planning these sessions, and also in giving papers at them. His discourses, according to Evans, "brought us new and stimulating ideas that deepened our understanding and appreciation of the science of topographic mapping." These ideas were the outgrowth of his own rich experience and of his acquaintance with mapping practices abroad and the current European literature. In his talks he reiterated his firm conviction that "topography is something more than engineering"; it partakes of "an interpretative and synthetic art." He insisted that "no topographer who would aspire to give maximum value to his work can hope to do so if he lacks an intelligent insight into the nature of land forms." The lack of such understanding on the part of the delineator "speaks from every line he draws; it betrays itself in the meaning-

François and Edith Matthes on Pinnacle Peak, near
Mount Rainier, Washington, August 12, 1911

less, wooden forms that characterize his sketches, in the evident crudeness of his conceptions of nature's work. These defects may pass unnoticed by the undiscerning, but they are nothing short of galling to those to whom every curve and flexure in a contour has a meaning."

In 1910 came Matthes' last major field assignment for the Topographic Branch, when he was put in charge of the mapping of yet another National Park, Mount Rainier, Washington. Once more he found himself working among glaciers, in this case the largest number to be found on any peak in the United States, many of them 6–8 miles long and covering, in the aggregate, 48 square miles. In his words, they "radiated like the arms of a great starfish." The rock cleavers between the glaciers offered a challenge to map maker and mountain climber alike. Inevitably his interest in glaciers and their work received fresh stimulus, and he again wrote several geological papers as the by-products of a topographic assignment.

Matthes made two ascents of Mount Rainier, each time back packing the heavy alidade and other equipment to the summit. On the first ascent, in 1910, he could accomplish little, as subfreezing temperatures and high winds made use of instruments impossible. On the second ascent, in 1911, he did a long day's work on the summit and made the perilous descent as darkness fell. Because of poor visibility, resulting from bad weather and forest fires, the field seasons of 1910 and 1911 permitted Matthes to complete little more than a fourth of the map (the southwestern part). The remaining part was completed in 1913 by others. The altitude of the mountain could then be determined. It proved to be 14,408 feet, the fourth highest peak in the continental United States.[3]

On June 7, 1911, François Matthes married Edith Lovell Coyle, a native of Washington, D. C., and a descendant of some of the founders and prominent citizens of the Virginia and Maryland colonies.

Edith Matthes was no stranger to the scientific world into which her marriage brought her, for she had been a librarian's assistant at the Smithsonian Institution. Among the interests which she and François had in common were love of the out-of-doors and appreciation of the beautiful in nature. Edith's wonderment and delight never ceased at François' ability to read nature as an open book, and their walks together, whether in the western mountains, over the sand dunes of Cape Cod, or through the by-paths of Rock Creek Park, at Washington, D.C., drew them together in an ever closer bond. Though never the thorough linguist that her husband was, Edith was well grounded in French and German, and in one other language, alien to François, Russian. Through travel abroad, including a sojourn of nearly two years in the capital of Russia, she had acquired a cosmo-

[3] The altitude of Mount Rainier was resurveyed in the summer of 1956 by a special joint survey party of the U. S. Geological Survey and the National Park Service. As a result, the altitude of Columbia Crest, the highest point on the mountain, was found to be 14,410 feet, rather than 14,408 feet. This left Mountain Rainier in fifth place, a position to which it was dropped in 1955 when a resurvey of Mount Harvard changed the altitude of that mountain from 14,399 feet to 14,420 feet. The order of the five highest peaks in the United States, exclusive of Alaska, is now as follows: Mount Whitney (14,495 feet), Mount Elbert (14,431 feet), Mount Harvard (14,420 feet), Mount Massive (14,418 feet), and Mount Rainier (14,410 feet). With the exception of Mount Whitney in California and Mount Rainier in Washington, these peaks are all in Colorado. (*Appalachia,* December, 1956, page 239.)

politanism akin to that of his. Most important of the influences she brought into his life were those stemming from warm sympathy and an intuitive understanding of his motivating hopes and purposes, as well as a home life unknown to him during the long years spent in western explorations.

For this bride now began a life very different from the one she had known in Washington and St. Petersburg. Immediately after their marriage, she accompanied her husband to Longmire, Washington, and all that field season shared with him the rigors of camp life on Mount Rainier. She learned to ride a horse and climb mountains, and she sat for long hours on the promontory stations taking down angles and working out elevations so as to permit the one paid assistant to map the streams and trails. In subsequent field seasons, whenever possible, Edith accompanied her husband on his pack-train expeditions, or she took up her abode at the farthest outpost of communications, there receiving the mail, attending to correspondence, and forwarding supplies to the camp. When the work was on the east front of the Sierra Nevada, more accessible by roads, she served unofficially as "chauffeur" of their personal car, specializing, as she put it, "in the business of navigating mountain passes and rutted roads," —and, it should be added, thereby leaving her husband free to study the landscape. Many an evening she spent in some lonely canyon as darkness fell, waiting in the car for François to come down off the mountains. By agreement the car doors were locked, and beside her on the seat lay the geologist's pick, her weapon of defense.

Matthes' concern with geomorphology had grown, year by year, and he had written and lectured extensively in this field. The series of charming geological essays he contributed to the Bulletin of the Sierra Club drew the attention of that organization to his work, especially since it related to the origin of Yosemite Valley, long a controversial question. On July 1, 1913, Matthes was transferred from the Topographic Branch of the Geological Survey to the Geologic Branch. It was the first such transfer to be made, and, though Matthes was now nearing forty, he welcomed the change as one which would enable him to give undivided attention to geologic problems, which by this time had become his primary interest. The many years he had devoted to topographic mapping gave him an unusual and, from many standpoints, an enviable background for the second phase of his career. Indeed, it may even be said that without that background some of his most significant contributions to geology could not have been made.

Matthes' interest in topographic mapping remained keen throughout his life. In taking geological field notes, as well as in other connections, he always found it most natural to resort to contour lines in depicting land forms. In 1919 he presented a paper before the Washington Academy of Sciences on "Relief Shading on Topographic Maps," a subject very near his heart and one in which he had long sought to arouse interest. When, eventually, the Geological Survey began publishing shaded topographic maps as standard practice, it was a source of great satisfaction to him.

Shortly before his death, Matthes presented to the Survey Library copies of the topographic maps of Yosemite Valley, and of the Yosemite and Mount Rainier National Parks, which he had shaded in pencil. The members of the map-shading unit of the Survey wrote him on this occasion, to express their appreciation of his skill, which, they held:

. . . despite much effort and study by contemporary advocates of the idea, has yet to be exceeded. It is with wonder and admiration that we, who now carry on this work, look upon the masterful understanding and quality exhibited in your work. . . . We just want you to know that you have real kindred spirits in our group who understand and appreciate what a pioneer you were in this field.

To the spokesman for this group, Matthes sent this message from his sick bed, on May 22, "I have never had a finer letter of appreciation from anyone and I want him to be sure to know how deeply touched I am by it."

Matthes' first geologic assignment was to study the origin of the Yosemite Valley and, what was without precedent, to report his findings in language understandable not only to scientists but to any intelligent and interested readers. He could hardly have dreamed, at the outset, how far afield this investigation would take him before he could reconstruct the sequence of dramatic events which had played a part in the making of what he liked to call "The Incomparable Valley." Not until sixteen years later, in the fall of 1930, did his completed report, the *Geologic history of the Yosemite Valley*, Professional Paper 160, come off the press. Professor Kirk Bryan,[4] in reviewing this most widely acclaimed of Matthes' publications, wrote, "Occasionally in the history of science there appears a work so excellent, so comprehensive, that it becomes immediately a classic. Such a newborn classic is the long-awaited 'professional paper' by Matthes on the Yosemite Valley."

It is not possible here to summarize Matthes' great monograph adequately; for that Professor Bryan's review should be consulted. It may be observed, however, that in Professional Paper 160 Matthes goes far beyond the limitations set by his title, for he interprets the Yosemite Valley in its relation to the

[4] *Journal of Geology,* volume 40, 1932, pages 84–87.

geologic history of the entire Sierra Nevada, giving special emphasis to problems of structure, geomorphology, and glacial geology. This he does, as Professor Bryan remarks, "with great breadth of insight and a wealth of detail, largely of a quantitative nature." It should be added that clues to the genesis of many geomorphic features of the Yosemite Valley, and thereby of other regions in the Sierra, were provided by the detailed petrographic studies of F. C. Calkins, published as a part of the report.

Matthes' attempt to address the widest possible circle of readers, by reducing to a minimum the use of "scientific jargon," was so successful that it has been emulated by many other writers; nevertheless, Professional Paper 160 remains the model in its field. It is not surprising, therefore, that the demand for this volume has exceeded that for any other Professional Paper. Copies of the first printing are now coveted by collectors of Californiana. The literary excellence of this work and Matthes' other writings is remarkable considering his late start in English; however, as he himself once observed, this was not wholly a handicap, for familiarity with other languages made one sensitive to subtle nuances of English which otherwise might pass undetected.

World War I brought Matthes special assignments, such as describing the geologic environments of Camp McClellan, Alabama, and Camp Gordon, Georgia. After the war, in the summer of 1919, the University of California Extension Division sponsored a series of lectures at Yosemite National Park, named after the noted professor, Joseph LeConte. Matthes was invited to present the geologic lectures and gave these on three successive days, July 8–10. The first and third lectures ("The Origin of the Yosemite Valley as Indicated in the History of Its Waterfalls," and "The Origin of the Granite Domes of the Yosemite") were given in the government pavilion in the valley, but the second lecture ("The Highest Ice Flood in the Yosemite Valley") was delivered out of doors to an audience which gathered at Glacier Point, 3200 feet above the valley floor, where use of lantern slides was needless as the landscape itself furnished the illustrations of the theme.[5]

Professional Paper 160, though a large volume, did not contain all the data which Matthes had gathered in the Sierra Nevada, for from the Merced and Tuolumne basins he had extended his investigations southward into the upper San Joaquin basin and even as far as the Kings Canyon and Sequoia National

[5] The LeConte Memorial Lectures were never published, as intended, but Matthes' contributions were in part included in Professional Paper 160 and in part published many years later (1950) in the posthumous volume, *The Incomparable Valley*.

Park. Through these reconnaissances he had become engrossed in the larger problems of Sierran geology and he was eager to pursue these further.

But there followed the "Mississippi Valley interlude," from 1928 to 1934, during which he was assigned to geologic problems in the Middle West. These put him far behind in his Sierran work—one reason why a number of his Sierran studies never were finished. In 1933 he did have opportunity to contribute two papers on the Sierra to Guidebook 16, prepared for an excursion of the Sixteenth International Geological Congress; and in 1935, to his great happiness, he was returned to California, this time through a co-operative agreement with the National Park Service, for a reconnaissance of Sequoia National Park. He completed this reconnaissance in 1936 and that summer also made investigations in the northern part of Yosemite National Park. The Sequoia data were urgently needed by the National Park Service, and to meet this need Matthes, pending opportunity to write a formal report, assembled three volumes which summarized the geology of the park by means of annotated photographs. These "Sequoia albums" proved invaluable and eventually, though not until two years after Matthes' death, were published in book form. Matthes was able to complete only one other major paper on Sequoia National Park, namely, *The Geologic History of Mount Whitney*, published in 1937.

In 1937 Matthes continued field work in Yosemite National Park and late in the summer began to investigate the east front of the Sierra Nevada. The resulting study he came to regard as the most important of his Sierran work, for it led him to conclude that the great eastern escarpment of the range had been formed as a result of early Pleistocene faulting, and hence was of much more recent origin than had been supposed. In 1938 and 1939 he was able to round out his evidence, at least in part. In July 1939, following meetings of the Cordilleran Section of The Geological Society of America, in Berkeley, where he presented his findings, he led a party, including several interested laymen, into the Yosemite Valley and thence across the range to the eastern escarpment itself, where the evidence could be reviewed on the spot. This was destined to be his last excursion into the Sierra Nevada.

Although in his later years Matthes published many papers, his time and strength were increasingly consumed by the demands of various scientific organizations. As chairman of the Committee on Glaciers of the American Geophysical Union, he organized and supervised a program for conducting co-öperative studies and measurements of the existing glaciers in the United States and abroad, a work which made him an international leader in deciphering "the elusive record of pre-historic, post-Pleistocene fluctuations of climate."[6] As a part of this program, he began assembling a collection of dated photographs and other records relating to the existing glaciers in the United States. This file has grown through the years and has become increasingly valuable for reference, revealing the changes in extent and volume which the glaciers have undergone. Also, Matthes prepared detailed reports summarizing and analyzing the data on glaciers, particularly with reference to their year-to-year changes, and these reports were published annually from 1932 to 1946 in the *Transactions* of the American Geophysical Union.

Matthes returned to Washington in the fall of 1939 at a time of world crisis. Hitler's hordes had invaded Poland, and the war in Europe was on. Delegates to the triennial assembly of the International Association of Scientific Hydrology were convening in the nation's capital. When the French secretary abruptly departed for his native land, Matthes—the only available linguist in the American delegation—was drafted to take his place. So he was burdened not only at these meetings but for years afterward with the responsibility for the activities of this group, one of the largest of international scientific organizations. He was also made secretary of the International Commission of Snow and Glaciers, another division of the Association, and this position likewise called for a tremendous amount of correspondence with scientific colleagues throughout the world.

On top of all this, Matthes was invited to write a chapter on glaciers, for

[6] Citation accompanying the Department of Interior honor award for distinguished service, with gold medal, conferred on François Matthes in April, 1948. The citation is published in the *Sierra Club Bulletin,* volume 33, 1948, page 8.

the volume on "Hydrology," Number IX, "Physics of the Earth" series, of the National Research Council. Review of the world-wide literature on glaciers, and the writing of the chapter, which itself grew to the size of a book, took practically all of 1941. This treatise, referred to in the *Quarterly Journal* of the Royal Meteorological Society (June 1949) as "a masterly summary of the characteristics and behavior of glaciers," Matthes himself considered to be his principal contribution to glaciology. In it, some of the ideas which had long been maturing in his mind received their fullest exposition, such as the view, now widely accepted, that most of the glaciers in the western United States are not the remnants of Pleistocene ice bodies, as previously assumed, but instead are "modern" glaciers which became re-ëstablished in post-Pleistocene time, probably as recently as within the last 4000 years, in what he aptly termed the "Little Ice Age."

During World War II, Matthes was called on to make many contributions to the war effort, including the work of the Military Geology Unit of the Geological Survey, by reason of his broad geographic knowledge and his command of foreign languages. In 1945, reluctantly but as a patriotic duty, he undertook a critical re-ëxamination of W. H. Hobb's doctrine of glacial anticyclones, which he regarded as scientifically untenable and indeed dangerous in that it afforded a false premise for the use of Greenland as an air base. In Part I of this study, published in 1946, he concluded that "there is no evidence of a virtually permanent 'glacial anticyclone' centered over the Greenland ice sheet. On the contrary . . . weather over the ice sheet is controlled by alternating cyclonic and anticyclonic movements. . . . Aviators need not expect so much as a fifty-fifty chance of meeting with good weather on flights across central Greenland, except for a few weeks in midsummer." Part II of this study was completed, after Matthes' death, by Arthur D. Belmont.

Matthes' versatility and manifold interests were not unmixed blessings. For instance, many of the innumerable requests for information received by the Geological Survey eventually found their way to his desk for reply. Such interruptions, although oft-times rewarding, were nevertheless distractions from his principal interests and could hardly do other than induce a certain sense of frustration. The brief years slipped away with the growing feeling that there was "so little time, so much to do."

Because of heavy demands made on the Geological Survey during and after the war, Matthes was continued on the active rolls somewhat more than three years beyond the statutory age of retirement (70 years), but on June 30,

1947, he retired. The summer was spent in Washington, winding up official and personal affairs. Finally, in September, François and Edith drove across the country to the little home in El Cerrito, California, which they had bought for the retirement years.

Matthes gave himself feverishly to the task of arranging his library and professional materials, took vigorous walks over the Berkeley Hills, and worked in the garden to "keep fit." In February, 1948, with long-deferred writing projects scarcely begun, he was handed a tremendous organizational task: to plan the program of the Committee on Snow and Glaciers for the sessions of the International Scientific Congress, scheduled to meet in August, at Oslo. He felt he would be derelict in his duty if he did not accept this task which, he knew, would require all his time and energies for months to come, but he did so with a heavy heart, seeming to sense that now his hopes for "the retirement years" might never be realized.

In the early morning hours of Sunday, April 18, Matthes was stricken with a heart attack. Nine weeks later, June 21, he died. On June 25, services were held at sunset in the El Cerrito home, high on the Berkeley Hills facing the Golden Gate, and later the ashes of François Matthes were brought to his beloved Yosemite. There, on September 18, in accordance with the wish he had expressed, that which was mortal of François Matthes was committed to "The Incomparable Valley."[7]

In the course of his life, recognition came to Matthes from many sources. He was starred in *American Men of Science*, and he served as president of the Geological Society of Washington in 1932 and of the American Association of Geographers in 1933. The long list of his affiliations with learned societies, mountaineering clubs, and other organizations, both domestic and foreign, can be found in *Who's Who in America*, and in *American Men of Science*, and need not be repeated here. Four honors may be mentioned as representative of the varied facets of his interests and work:

He was decorated Chevalier, Order of Leopold II, by King Albert of Belgium, in 1920, in appreciation of the account which he gave to the King and his party of the origin of Yosemite Valley, when they visited Yosemite in the autumn of 1919. He was awarded the Order of the Silver Beaver in 1931,

---

[7] François' twin brother, Gerard, outlived him by eleven years. His death occurred on April 8, 1959. "Memorial to Gerard Henrik Matthes, A Reclaimer of Rivers" (28 pages), by David E. Donley, was privately published by Mrs. Gerard H. Matthes in March, 1960. It includes a Selected Bibliography. A two-page abstract of this Memorial, prepared by Mrs. Gerard H. Matthes, was published by the American Society of Civil Engineers, as Memoir No. 2255.

by the Council of the Boy Scouts of America, for "distinguished service to boy-hood." This was the honor he cherished most dearly. At commencement exercises in the great stadium of the University of California in 1937 he was given the honorary degree of L.L.D. President Robert Gordon Sproul, in conferring the degree upon Matthes, said, in part, ". . . by your artistry in the delineation of land forms and your clear, scientific description, you have interpreted the beauty of the Western American Landscape to the mind as well as the eyes of all who love the mountains." Finally, on April 28, 1948, he was awarded the gold medal of the Department of the Interior for 51 years of distinguished service to the United States Government. The citation accompanying the award reached Matthes less than a month before his death, when he was gravely ill but not too ill to experience a glow of happiness when it was shown to him. The beautiful gold medal—a replica of the insignia of the Department of the Interior, showing in the foreground a bison in bas-relief, in the background a chain of mountain peaks silhouetted against the rays of the setting sun—did not come in time.

In 1949 the Sierra Club, which had been ever appreciative of its distinguished honorary vice-president, took measures to give the names "Matthes Crest" and "Matthes Lake" to two suitable geographic features in central Yosemite National Park.[8]

The place which François Matthes holds in American science is secure and, in certain respects, unique. He stands alone in having attained eminence first as topographer and later as geologist, and he is one of the relatively few whose writings rank as both science and literature. His colleagues held him in highest esteem not only for the originality and importance of his contributions to science but also because they knew him to be, at all times, a gentleman. Those who recall him from professional meetings will not forget the earnestness which distinguished his presentation of papers, his participation in discussions, and his assumption of the responsibilities so often entrusted to him.

Physically and intellectually alike, Matthes was impelled by a tremendous inner drive and tenacity of purpose; and his ideals with respect to workmanship were so high he was never willing to compromise short of the best results he could achieve. He was meticulous with respect to details, and conscientious and orderly to an extraordinary degree—traits well illustrated by his personal diary, which he began with an entry on January 1, 1897, the day he reported

[8] Moran, Reid V., Matthes Crest. *Sierra Club Bulletin*, volume 34, 1949, pages 110–111. An illustration of Matthes Crest appears in this volume, page 76.

for duty in Indian Territory, and continued uninterruptedly for more than fifty-one years. The final entry was made but two hours before he suffered the fatal heart attack.

In speech and manner, François Matthes retained a quaint suggestion of his rich inheritance of old-world culture, which clung to him like a fragrance. There was a certain dignity and courtliness about him; it might be described as a refinement which instinctively expressed itself in innate good taste and courtesy. He was aristocratic, but in the best sense of the word, for there was no snobbery about him. Through a long lifetime, he associated on terms of democratic equality with "all sorts and conditions of men," from kings to cooks.

François Matthes may have seemed, to some of his co-workers, a shy, almost aloof man; for he quietly went about his affairs, had no time or inclination for "small talk" during office hours, and worked with absorbed intensity at his desk or drafting table. Often he dined alone, seeming to be—as he actually was—deep in thought. But how his face brightened, and how animated his conversation became, when a former field associate called upon him, or someone broached a subject close to his heart!

There were facets to his personality which many colleagues never suspected, and relatively few understood, even among those who knew him intimately in a professional way. He was a highly sensitive person who rarely disclosed his innermost thoughts and feelings, and who, when he did so, could express himself better with pen than in speech. The aesthetic played a dominant part in his life; he was not only a scientist, but a poet, and an artist to the core. To a friend he confided, "I simply cannot be happy unless my work is conducted in country of inspirational beauty." During the "Mississippi valley interlude" he wrote to W. M. Davis, "I am temperamentally not well fitted for work on the monotonous flats of the Mississippi valley. . . . I should much prefer returning to the mountains and carrying on there as long as I am physically fit,—the more so if, coupled with the mountain work, there should be opportunity for contact with the public."

Among kindred spirits, Matthes was not shy. Actually, he loved people, especially young people; and in the many years of service he gave to scouting, Sierra Club activities, and the interpretative programs of the National Park Service, he found inner satisfactions which meant much to him. In his personal notes he recurs frequently to a theme expressed thus in one of his letters, "Nothing makes me happier than when I can share the results of my scientific studies with laymen." Those who knew Matthes only as the serious scholar might have been astonished at the gusto and enjoyment with which, on request, he would address tourists who packed the Yosemite Museum or gathered at an evening campfire to hear him recount the geologic history of Yosemite. He was a born teacher and might have accepted the teaching opportunities that came to him repeatedly had he not found the riddles of Sierra geology irresistibly fascinating. Francis P. Farquhar, California historian and former President of the Sierra Club, has written of Matthes that it was "a rare privilege to be with him and listen to his discourse. He was always glowing with enthusiasm and always eager to impart it to others. The beauty of the earth, particularly of mountains, moved him deeply, for he saw all around him manifestations of the orderly processes of creation."

In what someone once described as his "beautiful continental hand"—the hand in which he wrote out and painstakingly revised all his manuscripts, and which never lost its beauty or firmness despite the swiftness with which he wrote—Matthes was wont to copy those poems and passages which especially appealed to his thoughtful, beauty-loving, and deeply religious nature. These selections, and thoughts of his own which he jotted down on any piece of paper at hand, as they came to him, reveal the man. Thus, for a paper on Yosemite Valley he wrote a foreword (never published):

There are those who still fear that science will crush religion,—one hears not a little these days about 'those Godless scientists.' But pray, in what way can research of this sort possibly lead away from religion? Is it not, rather, a source of inspiration and spiritual growth which our very ignorance heretofore kept hidden from us? And does it not inevitably enhance our reverence for the Author of the universe?

On the wall of his room there hung, for almost four decades, a framed, illuminated copy of "The Footpath to Peace," by Henry Van Dyke, one of his favorite writers:

To be glad of life because it gives you the chance to love and to work and to play and to look up at the stars; to be satisfied with your possessions but not contented with yourself until you have made the best of them; to despise nothing in the world except falsehood and meanness, and to fear nothing except cowardice; to be governed by your admirations rather than by your disgusts; to covet nothing that is your neighbor's except his kindness of heart and gentleness of manners; to think seldom of your enemies, often of your friends, and every day of Christ; and to spend as much time as you can, with body and spirit, in God's out-of-doors—these are little guideposts to the path of peace.

In one of his notebooks François Matthes printed, with exquisite neatness, this verse by Irene Hardy:

> I follow the trail
> To find truth ere I rest.
> I follow the trail:
> Men say I shall fail
> In this measureless quest
> To find truth ere I rest.
> What though I fail?
> I follow the trail.

FRITIOF FRYXELL

Reprinted from Proceedings Volume of the Geological Society of America, Annual Report for 1955, pages 153–168. July, 1956. The sources on which this biographical account is based are given on page 153 of the Proceedings Volume, and a Selected Bibliography of the writings of Dr. Matthes appears on pages 166–168.

THE MARKS OF TIME

THE WINDS

OF THE

YOSEMITE VALLEY

To MOST PEOPLE roaming about the Yosemite Valley its winds and breezes seem a matter of small interest or consequence. They come and go, now one way, now another, apparently without regularity or system—moody, capricious beyond analysis. In the midst of the grand tumult of the Yosemite landscape, our senses fairly bewildered with its many glories, we cannot stop to consider these little breaths that blow about us, and let them puff by unheeded. The Yosemite region is not a windy country anyway; but once or twice in a season does a gale arise to disturb its wonted tranquillity, and its daily zephyrs are such light, airy little nothings as to scarcely seem worthy of downright study. And yet they become singularly interesting when once rightly understood. They turn out to be surprisingly systematic and withal so intimately connected with the configuration of the valley itself, that, to one who has at length mastered their secret they grow to be one of its immanent features, as characteristic and inseparable as El Capitan or the Yosemite Falls.

It happens to be so ordained in nature that the sun shall heat the ground more rapidly than the air. And so it comes that every slope or hillside basking in the morning sun soon becomes itself a source of heat. It gradually warms the air immediately over it, and the latter, becoming lighter, begins to rise. But not vertically upward, for above it is still the cool air pressing down. Up along the warm slope it ascends, much as shown by the arrows in the accompanying diagram (Fig. 1). Few visitors to the valley but will remember toiling up some never-ending zigzags on a hot and breathless day, with the sun on their backs and their own dust floating upward with them in an exasperating, choking

43

cloud. Perhaps they thought it was simply their misfortune that the dust should happen to rise on that particular day. It always does on a sun-warmed slope.

But again, memories may arise of another occasion when, on coming down a certain trail the dust ever descended with the travelers, wafting down upon them from zigzag to zigzag as if with malicious pleasure. That, however, undoubtedly happened on the shady side of the valley. For there the conditions are exactly reversed. When the sun leaves a slope the latter begins at once to lose its heat by radiation, and in a short time is colder than the air. The layer next to the ground then gradually chills by contact, and, becoming heavier

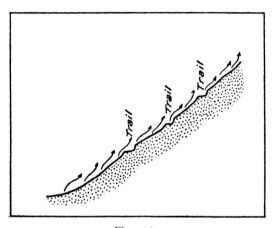

Figure 1

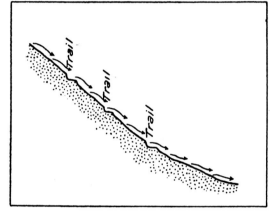

Figure 2

as it condenses, begins to creep down along the slope (Fig. 2). There is, thus, normally a warm updraft on a sunlit slope and a cold downdraft on a shaded slope—and that rule one may depend on almost any day in a windless region like the Yosemite. Indeed, one might readily take advantage of it and plan his trips so as to have a dust-free journey. One might time his ascent for an hour when the route lies wholly in the shadow; the dust will then obligingly pour over the edge of the trail, perhaps upon others following on a lower zigzag, but that, of course, is their lookout. Conversely one might time the descent for an hour when the trail is wholly in the sun. The dust will then float up behind one, leaving ever a clear path ahead. The writer, in fact, did deliberately put this in practice on more than one occasion during his sojourn in the valley, whenever the choice of hours mattered little otherwise—always with the desired result. Thus, he would be careful to make the ascent of the short trail to Glacier

Point before its zigzags emerged from the morning shadows, and to descend again before the sun had set on them. But the casual tourist is seldom favored in this way. His sight-seeing trips are laid out for him with little regard for any rules like these, and as a consequence, he eats Yosemite dust a good share of the time.

But, it may be objected, the valley sides lie ever part in the sun, part in shadow. The very lay and configuration of the valley are such that at no hour of the day is either of its slopes entirely sunlit; what with the many cliffs and headlands and recesses there is always a shadow here or there. Is there, then, really an updraft wherever the sun shines and a downdraft in every shadow patch? Most assuredly there is. That is one of the peculiarities of the valley, the immediate outcome of its exceptionally bold cliff topography. Every cliff that casts a shadow thereby creates a downward breeze. And thus, there are in spots throughout the valley local breezes that recur daily at certain hours as the shadows come and go. One may readily test this to his satisfaction on a place like Glacier Point. In the morning, when the great cliff is still in shadow, a bit of paper tossed over the brink at once disappears, sucked down by a descending current, but at noon when the sun beats on the cliff, the very opposite will happen; instead of sailing down, the paper shoots upward, and continuing upward, disappears like a tiny white speck in the blue.

But let it not be thought that there are none but local air currents in the valley. There is also a great general movement, itself the resultant of all the lesser ones. How it is brought about is not difficult to explain. As the afternoon wears on and the lengthening shadows advance over the landscape, the downward breezes progressively gain in force, extinguishing one after another the upward currents, until at last with the lowering of the sun they become general over the entire surface of the cooling land. Sliding down from every slope and cliff, they join in the bottom of the valley, there to form a broad airstream or river that flows on toward the plains below. Every side valley or canyon, moreover, sends its reinforcements, for in every one of them the same thing is happening; and thus, with nightfall there is organized a great system of confluent airstreams corresponding closely to the valley system of the land.

All night long this down-valley movement continues, until at length the morning brings the warming sun again. Then as summit after summit, and slope after slope is heated—insolated is the technical term—the warm updrafts are revived again. At first feeble and in spots only, they soon wax stronger and more general, and, as the shadows retreat and dwindle before the oncoming light invasion, they finally gain the upper hand. The nocturnal airstreams cease to flow and a general movement is inaugurated in the opposite direction, up toward the highlands at the valley head. It is not usually so noticeable as the night wind, for its tendency is naturally to spread and diffuse upward, while the nocturnal movement is one of condensation and concentration, especially vigorous along the valley floor. But it is none the less a well-defined, characteristic movement that continues throughout the day. Late in the afternoon, with the growing of the shadows it gradually comes to a stop and the tide turns back again. Thus the air of the Yosemite Valley goes through a daily ebb and flood, reversing early every morning and again late in the afternoon.

Most mountain valleys have similar alternating night and day winds, but those of the Yosemite Valley are exceptionally pronounced. All conditions in its case favor the orderly consummation of the process and conspire to accentuate each phase. No general winds sweep over the country to interfere with the local up- or downdrafts, except at intervals of many weeks; and so exceedingly dry and pure is the atmosphere of the Sierra, so few particles of dust or moisture does it hold, that the sun's rays plunge through it almost without let or hindrance. Insolation, consequently, is particularly intense and begins almost immediately with the rising of the sun, while radiation is equally rapid and sets in promptly the moment the sun disappears. And thus it comes that the reversals in the Yosemite Valley take place with clock-like regularity, and the entire movement assumes the rhythmic swing of a pendulum. Nothing was better calculated to make this visible to the eye than the smoke column from the forest fires that raged persistently at the lower end of the valley during the summer of 1905. Every morning the valley was clear, having been swept out, so to speak, by the nocturnal down-valley current, and the smoke pall could be seen floating off to the southwest, low down on the Sierra flank. But with the rising of the warm day breezes the smoke would gradually advance up the valley, becoming denser by degrees, until by nine or ten o'clock one could scarcely see across from rim to rim. This condition would prevail all day until with the afternoon reversal the down-valley wind would set in again and take the smoke back with it. Much to the chagrin of the writer, who at the time was engaged in the survey of the valley and depended on the clearness of the air for his long distance sights, this daily smoke invasion persisted for four long months with scarce an interruption. It may be imagined that he came to understand the phenomenon right well.

Half Dome from the top of Yosemite Falls. By J. N. LeConte

Oddly enough, it is precisely upon this daily atmospheric seesaw that one of the Yosemite's chief attractions depends. As is well known, one must go to Mirror Lake at an early morning hour, if he wishes to see it at its best. The surprised and usually somewhat vexed tourist who finds he must arise at an impossible hour in order to enjoy a perfect reflection, little dreams that what he is undertaking really amounts to keeping a tryst with the early morning reversal out on the shores of Mirror Lake; and that, unless he be quite punctual he will miss it because of its almost momentary briefness. Yet such is actually the case. The stillness of the water surface sets in just as the down-valley draft dies out; but as soon as the upper cliffs or Tenaya Canyon become sufficiently insolated, updrafts begin to stir the air again, and a faint tremor forthwith steals over the lake. Accepting the correctness of this explanation, one is tempted to believe there might be another calm corresponding to the afternoon reversal,—an ever so much more convenient hour for the tourist. But alas, experience has shown that this cannot always be depended on. The reason is, no doubt, that in the afternoon there is no well-defined pause in the circulation of the air of Tenaya Canyon, because of the presence of great shadows on its north side which send down eddying breezes at various times.

This discussion of the winds of the Yosemite Valley would scarcely be complete without a word about the breezes that play near the great waterfalls. Each of these, it will be remembered, leaps from the mouth of an elevated hanging valley. At night, when the down-valley currents are organized, the stream issuing from each of these valleys plunges down over the cliff very much like a waterfall. Few people probably are aware of the existence of these—shall we call them "air falls"? Nevertheless, they are by no means imaginary, as one may readily find out by ascending either the Yosemite Falls trail or the Nevada Fall trail in the evening. The writer had occasion to do so many times when returning to his high-level camps above the valley, and the unpleasant memory of the chilling downdrafts that poured upon him on these evening trips is with him yet. During the daytime, on the other hand, the air rises vertically along the cliffs and up into the hanging valleys, taking part of the spray from the falls along with it. A pretty example of this may be seen at the Bridalveil Fall, where two little combs of spray, one on each side of the stream, steadily curve upward over the brink. As soon as the sun is off the cliff, however, they at once cease to exist.

Reprinted from Sierra Club Bulletin, *June, 1911, pages 91–95.*

THE STRIPED ROCK FLOOR

OF THE

LITTLE YOSEMITE VALLEY

ABOUT a stone's throw from where the Clouds Rest Trail leaves the flat of the Little Yosemite Valley, there is a curious expanse of smooth, bare granite, an acre or more in extent. It is a part of the solid rock floor of the valley, which, buried under river gravel and glacial material elsewhere, is here exposed to view, cleared of all debris. Indeed, so scrupulously clean swept does it look, one might fancy some cyclopian broom had been at work on it—and a new one at that.

Round about, in all directions lie glacial boulders, some singly, some in clusters, some in heaps mixed with fine debris. Sparse pines and cedars rise from what few cracks the stone floor affords as a root-hold, giving the place a singularly genial, parklike aspect. But the cleared tract itself has not a tree on it—its surface stretches unbroken and continuous, unmarred by a single fissure.

As one approaches from the lower end and looks up the gentle slope—for the floor inclines appreciably—the eye is almost at once held by the peculiar "painted" appearance of the space. Irregular, blotchy white ribbons set off conspicuously against the prevailingly gray tint of the rock floor, sprawl over it here and there. Wholly unlike the dark water stains that stripe most of the Yosemite cliffs, they seem, even to one thoroughly familiar with the various markings common to the rock surfaces of the region, altogether novel and enigmatic. All trend downward with the slope, but beyond this there seems no discoverable law in their arrangement, nor anything else immediately suggestive of their mode of origin. The majority occur in loosely connected groups, but some lie off by themselves, like pale islands in a dark ocean. As the view on page 51 well shows, they generally commence abruptly and terminate abruptly, without definite relation to the unevenesses of the floor itself. Some divide, others merge downward; some gain in width, others taper down toward their lower ends.

In dimensions they are equally varied. While they average between four and five feet in length and from two to three inches in breadth, there are individuals among them but a fraction of a foot long and others exceeding twelve or even fifteen feet; and some are less than an inch across, while others—like those in the immediate foreground of the view—span six inches and over. Nor is the breadth always proportionate to the length: Some of the longest are very narrow, some of the shortest very broad.

On closer inspection they are seen to consist simply of narrow tracts from which the lichens that otherwise uniformly mottle the rock have been removed, and it becomes plain that it is merely the light color of the unweathered granite thus exposed that makes them prominent. These stripes, then, are not stains at all; rather, they owe their brilliancy to their very stainlessness—to the absence of coloring matter of any sort.

By what agent the lichens were cleared off, however, seems at first a mystery. That it was some substance that moved downhill under the influence of gravity is patent from the invariable downhill trend of all the stripes, but what the nature of that substance was, is not easily guessed. One feels tempted to believe it was some corrosive fluid that was poured out upon the rock and flowed down slowly, eating away the lichens as it went. There are places in the Yosemite Valley where such a thing has actually happened, so the theory is not so utterly absurd as at first blush it may seem. On the road to Mirror Lake, for instance, there is a great block of granite on the flat side of which some enterprising individual once painted him an advertisement in bold, glaring type. The true history of the affair may be better known to some of the readers of this journal than to the writer, but he gathers from a casual look that the "ad" was subsequently effaced by a zealous guardian. Whatever material the latter employed to remove the paint, removed the lichens too, running down in vertical, blotchy stripes remarkably similar to those on the Little Yosemite floor. Again, at the site of the "Old Blacksmith Shop," near the foot of the Coulterville Road, a space has been cleared on a huge rock by means of some caustic, and the same streaky effect has been produced.

But the stripes in the Little Yosemite Valley clearly were not the work of marring man. Besides, the same sort of markings exist in many other places in the Yosemite region, in seldom frequented spots too, as a rule. It was on such a spot, in fact—on the north slope of Liberty Cap—that the writer first found a clue to their mode of origin. A small rock fragment, derived from a disintegrating shell of the great rock hump, had evidently slid here several feet from its place of starting, and, extending from it, pointing up the slope, was a little white path cleared of lichens. Not far away were other fragments each likewise leaving a flaming trail. The width of the stripe produced corresponded in each case to the dimensions of the fragment. A tiny bit of granite, no larger than a thimble, lay at the end of a delicate white ribbon, and an uptorn tree stump had made a dozen markings, one with each of its dragging root tips and a broad swath with its heavy broken end. Surely, here was the key to the enigma! Here were the stripes in process of being made.

What, however, impelled the rocks and the tree stump downward? None of them appeared in motion, and none when dislodged, would slip or roll. The slope was not steep enough for that. Observation further showed that no stripes ever occur on very steep slopes—they are restricted to surfaces of moderate inclination such as the crowning portions of the domes, and wherever the declivity approaches the "angle of repose" the stripes invariably come to an end. A pretty and striking instance was seen on a small dome spur in the Little Yosemite Valley. Here the stripes, diverging downward like meridians on a globe, all terminated abruptly as by concert at the same level, the same parallel of latitude. Below that line, evidently, the debris had slid or rolled away. The inclination here, it should be noted, was too gr   ʾ to stand on safely, but farther up, among the stripes, one could walk even with ʾobnails by exercising a little care.

It is to be inferred from the above that a slow motion of the debris is essential for the production of the stripes. The explanation is here offered that the debris

hese mysterious stripes on the floor of Little Yosemite alley are narrow paths from which slow-growing lichens ve been removed.

Snow and running water have slowly pushed this small boulder across the gently sloping granite, wearing away the lichens.

is urged down little by little by snow and running water and even the rockgrains washing from above, in fact by all agents coöperating with gravity to overcome the frictional resistance of the floor. Most potent, no doubt, are the heavy snows of winter, and there is good reason to believe the greatest progress is made under their influence. For, on inclined surfaces of this sort, snow does not lie wholly inert, but almost imperceptibly creeps downward—the same as it does on the roofs of barns and sheds. As the entire layer advances, it naturally tends to drag the debris with it.

The total progress thus effected may not exceed an inch or two per year, and this estimate, if it is at all correct, lends additional significance to the stripes: they indicate not merely the route traveled over by each fragment, they also embody a time record of the journey. Some of them represent a lapse of many years, the more impressive when it is reflected that during all that time no being, human or other, happened by in this solitude to interfere with the orderly continuance of the process.

The explanation above, however, accounts only for the movement of the debris. It does not yet make clear the production of the stripes themselves. That a heavy boulder might grind off the lichens from the bed it passes over seems quite natural, but that a bit of rock weighing an ounce or two should clear a path does not seem at all self-evident. The weight of the fragment, if it is a factor in the process, apparently plays but a minor role.

On picking up one of these traveling fragments, one finds it invariably imbedded in a small pad of loose rock grains that have collected under it. Now lichens cannot thrive under the thinnest veneer of sand or soil, as may be observed in a thousand places throughout the Sierra. Slanting rocks uncovered by the grading of a wagon road, for instance, show plainly by the boundary of their lichen growth where the surface of the ground used to be. Shallow basins in a rock floor or on large boulders that tend to accumulate sand, pine needles, and other litter, similarly remain white and bare of lichens. It is safe to say, therefore, that it is the sand pad under the fragments rather than the fragments themselves that clears the lichens from the stripes. And here, again, is substantiation of the view expressed regarding the slowness of the process. For, were the movement at all rapid, the lichens in any one spot would not remain covered for a sufficient length of time to utterly die and loose their hold. As a matter of fact there are places where they were not entirely stamped out and the stripes appear dim or interrupted. The debris must have advanced here with more than usual rapidity, owing to some local acceleration of the gradient, or perhaps through the pressure of an exceptionally heavy snow fall.

To come back now to the floor of the Little Yosemite Valley equipped with this insight into the stripe-producing process, let us look it over somewhat more closely. The feature that strikes us as most puzzling is the total absence of debris of any kind. Whatever material once traveled over the floor has in some manner disappeared. But not wholly, for here, near the east edge of the tract, lies a boulder weighing some twelve or fifteen pounds at the end of a long and glorious stripe. More than twenty feet it stretches, gradually fading in the distance like the smoke trail of a locomotive. A finer example would be difficult to find. The upward dimming of the stripe is in itself significant: so excessively slow has the progress of the boulder been that the lichens are already beginning to encroach again on the upper end, slow-growing plants though they be. When it is considered that rocks uncovered by road grading a score of years ago show scarcely any new lichens today, the great span of time represented by this stripe become doubly impressive. Its upper end, indeed, may date back to the time the Yosemite Valley was discovered.

But this stripe, after all, differs somewhat from the others on the floor. The rank and file are shorter and narrower; many split or fork irregularly, and all have ceased to grow in length through the removal of the debris that made them. Yet that material did not roll away, for the floor maintains about the same grade throughout and many stripes begin in the same latitude where others end. How, then, are these traits to be interpreted?

In the first place it seems certain that the material in question consisted of small, light fragments that were easily disturbed and thrown from their path by the feet of passing men or animals. That this must have happened more than once seems likely in view of the fact that the Little Yosemite is much frequented and in former days was inhabited by Indians, as the round holes in which they ground their acorns, near by, amply attest.

Again, the assumption seems legitimate that the fragments were in an advanced state of disintegration, and broke down and crumbled on the way. Much of the debris that litters the valley floor today is in just such a crumbly state. It has lain exposed so long to strong diurnal and seasonal temperature changes that the individual crystals in the granite, each expanding and contracting with a coefficient of expansion peculiar to the mineral composing it—feldspar, quartz, mica or hornblende,—have gradually worked loose and are ready to part company. Those readers who have mountaineered in the Sierra may have had the experience of picking up a rock that would break in the hand and run like sand through the fingers. This suggests an explanation for the forking of the stripes: A decomposing fragment, after having advanced some distance, would break in two. From then on there would be a double trail. Later, each of the pieces would divide, and the trail would split again. Some fragments broke down by degrees into an aggregate of half-loose crystals, and their trails widened out progressively. The end in each case came no doubt, when there was nothing left but a little heap of rock grains which the melting waters of springtime carried off with a rush.

Reprinted from Sierra Club Bulletin, *January, 1911, pages 3–9. See also Matthes' paper "Debris Tracks on the Domes of the Yosemite Region,"* Science, n.s., *Volume XXX, Number 758, pages 61–64, 1909.*

EL CAPITAN MORAINE
AND ANCIENT
LAKE YOSEMITE

IT SEEMS well nigh unbelievable in these days of enlightenment that so eminent a scientist as the late Professor J. D. Whitney should have seen fit to deny the former existence of glaciers in the Yosemite Valley. Said he in his famous old Guide Book: "A more absurd theory was never advanced than that by which it was sought to ascribe to glaciers the sawing out of these vertical walls and the rounding of the domes. Nothing more unlike the real work of ice, as exhibited in the Alps, could be found. Besides, there is no reason to suppose, or at least no proof, that glaciers have ever occupied the valley or any portion of it . . ."

As a matter of fact, there are excellent reasons for believing that the Yosemite Valley was once invaded by ice, and the proofs of its glacial occupancy are abundant and indubitable. The wonder is that Whitney could have overlooked them.

The very shape of the valley, trough-like, steep-sided, clean-cut; the great height of the hanging valleys from whose lips the thundering waterfalls pour; the giant stairway down which the Merced River tumbles in its descent from the Little Yosemite; these features are, on the face of them characteristically glacial, and impressively attest the great magnitude of the erosional work done by the ice.

But perhaps the skeptical reader would prefer evidences of a more tangible sort, more immediately linkable with the intimate form and habits of glaciers, and demanding less from the imagination in the way of appraisal of the capacity of glaciers to erode, a subject on which even those best qualified to judge are by no means united.

Distant Storm Front, Yosemite Valley, California. By Ansel Adams

Allow me to invite him to the floor of the Yosemite Valley, and, with our backs turned to the lofty hanging valleys and their eloquent cataracts, let us search for the less spectacular but more direct, and perhaps more convincing, proofs of ice work which there exist.

If we should set up a surveyor's level in the meadows opposite the Sentinel Hotel and thence run down the valley, taking careful elevations on the way, we would find the altitude to remain essentially unchanged for miles. Indeed, as far as the El Capitan bridge there is no appreciable fall to the valley floor, and the Merced River meanders dreamily, in lazily swinging, sandy loops and curves. At the El Capitan bridge, however, there is an abrupt change. The stream awakens, as if refreshed from its nap in the valley, and with quickened pace, dashes over riffles and churns among boulders, tumbling lustily like a youthful mountain torrent. Its fall becomes rapid, fifty to one hundred feet per mile, whereas above the bridge, in a distance of six miles, it descends only about six feet.

Evidently, the El Capitan bridge marks a critical point in the course of the river and a dividing line in the valley itself. Broad and level above the bridge, below it the valley can scarcely be said to have any floor at all. Even the Bridalveil Meadows, which occupy the widest place, slant strongly toward the river, being a debris fan built by Bridalveil Creek. Farther down, the valley sides close in from either side and the river lies constrained in the bottom of a narrow V.

What may be the cause of this abrupt change of scene at the El Capitan bridge? No doubt many of the readers of the *Bulletin* have passed back and forth over that bridge, but probably few have taken careful notice of its peculiar location. The writer himself did not become aware of the significance of the site until after a sojourn of several months.

It was no mere whim that led Galen Clark to select that spot for a bridge. A strong ridge of boulders here lies athwart the floor of the valley, and it is across the gap in that ridge, worn through by the stream, that the bridge has been thrown.

South of the El Capitan bridge the grading of the wagon road has necessitated cutting away part of the ridge, but the huge boulders, of which it is largely composed, may be seen in the side of the cut. Climbing out of the road, one may follow the curving crest for a few hundred feet until it becomes lost in the coarse debris at the base of the Cathedral Rocks.

North of the river, the ridge runs west of the road, stretching across the valley for half a mile like a steep-sided, narrow-crested embankment. At first fully fifteen feet high, it gradually loses in height and prominence, and finally, toward the road forks, appears to die out altogether. However, it does not end here, but merely becomes buried under the toe of the huge debris slopes descending from the cliffs about Ribbon Fall.

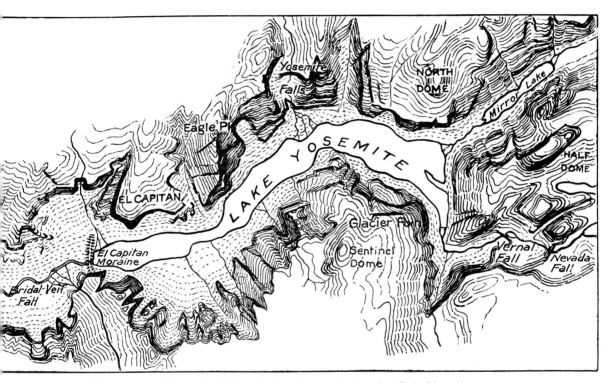

Sketch-map of Yosemite Valley, showing the extent of ancient Lake Yosemite

Were this peculiar ridge, unique in the configuration of the valley floor, situated in the open so that its form stood out conspicuously above the surrounding flat, no doubt from the first it would have attracted attention; its significance would have been looked into and now would be common knowledge. As it is, dense thickets of pine and cedar effectually mask the ridge; most passers-by are not aware of its existence, and even some of the scientists who have studied the valley in detail have missed the feature and thereby the key to the recent geological history of the entire valley floor.

The boulder ridge in question is a typical glacial moraine; no experienced glacialist would for a moment hesitate in identifying it as such. It is a terminal moraine, properly speaking,—that is, a debris ridge of the sort which glaciers commonly build up at their fronts. All glaciers, as is well known, carry a considerable amount of rock debris derived from the floor and sides of the valleys through which they advance, and this material, as the ice melts away, is released at the lower end. While the front of a glacier is inherently subject to frequent oscillations, some years melting back, at other times advancing, there are nevertheless occasional periods of relative constancy during which the front remains stationary, or very nearly so. It is then that this ice-freed debris accumulates in the form of an embankment or morainic ridge, as it is technically termed. When, moreover, the period of quiescence follows immediately upon one of advance and pronounced erosional activity, during which the glacier heavily loaded itself with debris, the moraine is likely to assume proportions that will enable it to endure as a topographic feature of some permanence.

This, in fact, is what occurred in the Yosemite Valley. When the ice front receded for the last time—there were several separate glacial epochs—it made a number of minor readvances, following one upon the other like so many gradually dying pulsations. Each of these readvances left a separate moraine, and accordingly a number of such ridges are found spaced at intervals across the valley floor. All of them are situated in the lower half of the valley, and the moraine at the El Capitan bridge, which may appropriately be called the El Capitan moraine, is the uppermost, the youngest of the series.

It is also the strongest, the most perfectly preserved of all. The other moraines today are represented only by truncated fragments, their major portions having been broken down and swept away by the swollen river. Around the broken end of one of these ridges, projecting from the extreme northwest corner of the Cathedral Rocks, the wagon road swings as it bends southward to the Bridalveil Fall.

The El Capitan moraine, it appears, not only escaped the partial demolishment that overtook its brethren, but, by virtue of its strength and peculiar situation, became a factor of importance in the post-glacial remodeling of the valley bottom. Stretching across the valley from wall to wall, like an unbroken dam, it ponded the waters behind it, and, as the ice melted back, transformed the upper Yosemite Valley into a lake.

This sheet of water—Lake Yosemite, it may aptly be called—like most lakes of a similar origin, was not destined to endure. No sooner had it come into existence than the Merced River, turbid with debris from the glaciers farther up, proceeded to build a delta at the upper end, and this delta, slowly but inexorably advancing, in time wholly extinguished the lake.

The manner in which the filling was accomplished one may today watch in Mirror Lake. Already reduced from a sheet of water more than a mile long, this little lake, famous for its reflections, is annually being diminished in area by an appreciable amount through the rapid forward growth of the delta of Tenaya Creek. Measurements of the delta front for a few consecutive years would afford a basis for an estimate of the length of time that the lake is likely to continue to delight the visitor with its beautiful reflections.

Although nothing now remains of ancient Lake Yosemite, its extent, nevertheless, is still easily ascertained. One need but follow the edge of the level meadows that now form the valley floor, in order to trace the former shore line. Evidently the lake occupied the entire extent of the valley, up to the cliffs that enclose its head; its length, therefore, must have been close to six miles.

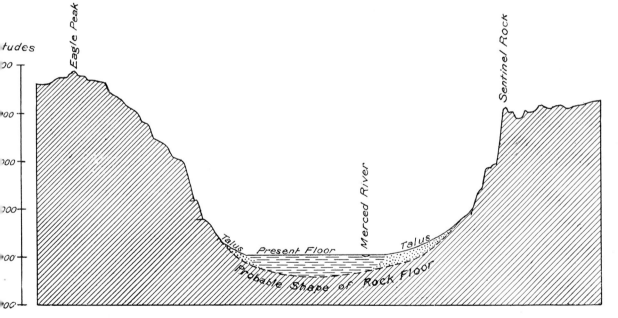

Section of Yosemite Valley from Eagle Peak to Sentinel Rock, showing 1913 estimate of probable depth of river sediment filling the basin of ancient Lake Yosemite. Seismic soundings have subsequently indicated a much deeper excavation (see page 62).

Nor was it a mere shallow pool. Its depth, there are reasons for believing, may have exceeded 500 feet. No actual measurements, such as might be obtained by borings, for instance, are available, it is true, and the figure mentioned cannot claim to be any more than a mere estimate. Yet it is not wholly without foundation, as a glance at the accompanying diagram has shown. That diagram represents one of a number of cross-sections of the valley, constructed by the writer with the accurate and abundant trigonometric data on which the detail map of the Yosemite Valley is based. Being free from vertical exaggeration, it affords a fair means for judging the probable depth of sediment now filling the valley. It is reasonable to assume that the Yosemite Valley, having been vigorously glaciated, possesses a somewhat concave rock floor, shaped like the bottom part of a U. Completing, tentatively, the missing part of the curve, therefore, one obtains an approximate measure of the depth of the extinct lake. In the cross-section published herewith, the curve has purposely been drawn quite flat, in order that the estimate of depth may not be accused of undue liberality. Yet, the depth indicated by the diagram is not far from 500 feet. Other cross-sections give closely accordant figures, those toward the head of the valley indicating still greater depths.

Is it to be inferred also, the question may here be asked, that the El Capitan moraine has a height of 500 feet? No, that ridge, in all probability, does not stand a hundred feet high above its base. A direct measurement of its height, unfortunately, cannot be had. The river has not yet cut the notch down to bed rock. At least so Galen Clark informed the writer. While still in charge of the valley, he had undertaken to enlarge the notch in order to lessen the danger from floods during the spring freshets. He had found only loose boulders, which he had removed with the aid of dynamite.

On its up-stream side the ridge is buried under lake deposits, and only the upper fifteen feet emerge. On its down-stream side it slopes down twenty-five to thirty feet, but there, too, its foot is covered by river gravels of unknown depth. Examination of other moraines in the Yosemite region, more especially those of the later ice invasions, to which the El Capitan moraine itself belongs, seems to indicate, however, that a height of one hundred feet is the maximum assignable. The majority of these ridges scarcely exceed fifty or sixty feet in height. Five-hundred-foot moraines are foreign to the region.

If the El Capitan moraine is not over one hundred feet high, how, then, shall we account for the great depth of Lake Yosemite, as indicated by the diagram?

The answer is, by assuming the existence of a deep basin eroded in the rock floor of the valley by the ice. There is nothing violent in that assumption. Glaciers normally excavate extensive rock basins in the bottom of their valleys. The well-attested instances of such action are literally numberless. Lake basins are a familiar feature of all glaciated mountain regions, and in some cases—such as that of Lake Chelan—they occur on a truly stupendous scale, dwarfing Lake Yosemite into insignificance.[1]

Nor need one go outside the Yosemite region for examples. There is evidence of a lake basin on every tread of the stairwise descending branch canyons. The stair-like character of the floors of these canyons, it may be pointed out in passing, is a distinctly glacial trait, and the presence of lake basins hollowed out in the treads is only one of the concomitant features.

Thus the entire Little Yosemite Valley was once occupied by a lake. Filled with river gravels, like the main valley itself, it now presents the appearance of a gradeless flat of some three miles, above which only the crests of several curving terminal moraines emerge.

On the tread immediately above the Vernal Fall, again, is Emerald Pool, diminutive, yet as typical a glacial rock basin as one can find anywhere. Tenaya Canyon, it appears, once possessed four glacial lakes, situated at successively higher levels. All but the lowest, however, are now filled with sediment; Mirror Lake alone survives as a remnant of the largest lake.

After one has become familiar with all these lake basins in the branch canyons of the Yosemite Valley, and one has, moreover, gained an insight into their mode of origin, one can scarcely avoid reaching the conclusion that in the main valley, too, there is a deeply eroded rock basin, now covered by the silts of Lake Yosemite. The combined mass of the Tenaya and Merced glaciers here must have eroded with particular vigor. The very fact that each of these ice streams, by itself, was able to excavate rock basins of considerable extent and depth, leaves little doubt that united they achieved still larger erosional results. Besides, it has been noted that it is immediately below the confluence of glaciers that the ice usually attains the greatest power to excavate.

[1] The writer's attention has been called to what appears to be rock-in-place visible in the bed of the Merced in the upper part of the valley. The supposed great depth of sedimentary filling in the valley would thereby seem to be discredited. A visit to the spot in the fall of 1910, however, enabled the writer to satisfy himself that the outcrop of rock reported is in reality only an indurated bed of coarse river sand, irregularly gullied out by the current, and closely resembling solid granite. It is friable in the hand and is underlain by unconsolidated layers of sand and silt.

The El Capitan moraine, then, is not to be given sole credit for the creation of Lake Yosemite. That lake in all probability lay in a rock basin eroded by the ice, and the only function of the moraine dam was to raise the level of the waters, thus increasing their depth and extent.

In the meanwhile it should not be forgotten that the existence of the rock basin is purely inferential and is to be considered unproven until a series of borings along the whole length of the valley shall afford the necessary facts. It is to be hoped that some day such borings may be undertaken; they would not merely serve to solve a problem of great local interest, but would contribute much-desired data regarding the still challenged eroding efficiency of glaciers.

That the Yosemite Valley has actually been occupied by glacial ice no one will venture to dispute; were all other ice signs in the valley rejected as untrustworthy, the El Capitan moraine alone would afford evidence sufficient and irrefutable. As to the extent to which the ancient glaciers have remodeled and excavated the valley, nothing, perhaps, would go further toward settling this vexed question than a series of direct measurements establishing beyond doubt the depth of former Lake Yosemite.[2]

Reprinted from Sierra Club Bulletin, *January, 1913, pages 7–15.*

[2] The borings which Matthes hoped might eventually give conclusive answers to questions concerning the depth of Lake Yosemite, the fill of sediments in Yosemite Valley, and the depth and configuration of the bedrock floor beneath, have yet to be made. However, from another quarter, undreamed of in 1913 when Matthes published this essay, have come significant data relating to these questions, namely seismic soundings at many points on the valley floor. These soundings were made in 1935 and 1937, and the resultant technical report ("Seismic Explorations on the Floor of Yosemite Valley, California," by Beno Gutenberg, John P. Buwalda, and Robert P. Sharp. *Bulletin of the Geological Society of America,* Volume 67 [August, 1956], pages 1051–1078) may be consulted by readers interested in the detailed interpretations drawn from the seismic data. The introduction says:

"For fully 50 years earth scientists have differed strongly as to the efficacy of glacial erosion. One discussion of considerable warmth centered on Yosemite Valley, which Muir stoutly maintained was largely the product of glacial sculpturing and which Whitney contended was a product of tectonic subsidence. Other workers thought that erosion by running water and moving ice had done the job, but it remained for Matthes to show that these two agents played essentially equal parts in creating Yosemite Valley. Matthes' work is an outstanding attempt at a quantitative estimate of the magnitude of glacier excavation based on geological evidence.

"The seismograph shows that even Matthes, an enthusiastic glacial sculpturist, underestimated by a full order of magnitude the amount of glacial excavation on the bedrock floor of Yosemite Valley. Where he estimated 450 m of deepening by glaciers, at least another 550 m must be added. Where Matthes estimated the unconsolidated valley fill to be 90 m it is closer to 600 m. Thus, the steep granitic walls rising 900 m above the present valley bottom are more than 1500 m above the bedrock floor. The visitor sees but three-fifths the splendor and magnitude. . . .

"Yosemite Valley is thus an outstanding example of the efficacy of glacial excavation in overdeepening valleys and in creating large closed depressions. It is comparable in this respect to Lake Chelan, the Great Lakes, the Finger Lakes, and many fiords." (References omitted from quotation.)

THE STORY
OF MORAINE DOME

Surmounting the north wall of the Little Yosemite Valley—the "ante-chambre" through which the Merced River approaches the Yosemite Valley proper—is a rounded eminence of bare granite, a typical dome of the kind so common in the central Sierra Nevada. Fully 2000 feet high above the floor of the Little Yosemite, it rises to an elevation of 8012 feet, to within a hundred feet, in other words, of the level of Sentinel Dome, the favorite panoramic view point of the tourist; yet it is an inconspicuous feature in the landscape, a mere wave in the billowy highland that stretches on either side of the valley trough. The towering bulk of the Clouds Rest massif, about a mile to the northward, further dwarfs it into insignificance; and thus, being remarkable neither for height nor for scenic assets, this unobtrusive little dome has remained generally unnoticed and unknown. Indeed, until quite recently, it did not even possess a name. Yet, to him who sees and knows, it is a place of peculiar if not unique interest, well worthy of a pilgrimage. There are other qualities besides spectacular height and scenic charm that attract one to some spots.

It was in 1906, at the time when the topographic survey of the Yosemite Valley was in full swing, that a party of surveyors one hot summer day approached this height, intending to make an instrument station on the summit. Keen to select an easy route for the ascent with their heavy plane-table outfit, they resolved to take advantage of what appeared to be a massive, tree-grown embankment that wound in a long smooth curve up the bulging south side of the dome (see photos on pages 66 and 67). Some 40 feet high, it rose with steady, uninterrupted grade, as if laid by a careful engineer, carrying its strip of forest with it across the bare, sun-baked granite slope; and thus, by easy stages and under genial shade, the party reached a point less than a hundred and fifty feet below the summit. There the ridge came abruptly to an end, cut off by a precipice that fell off sheer almost 2000 feet to the valley floor below.

63

Prof. A. C. Lawson[1]   Washington, D. C.
University of California   Jan. 24, 1915
Berkeley, Calif.

My dear Prof. Lawson:

I am sending you by registered mail the manuscript of a paper on Moraine Dome which I had prepared for the *Sierra Club Bulletin*. (Through various delays it could not be finished in time to be included in the January issue, but I shall reserve it for the next one).

I believe you may like to read it over, as it deals with the question of multiple glaciations in the Sierra Nevada. The Moraine Dome locality is of special interest in that it shows with considerable clearness the contrast in the age of the older and younger moraines. In fact, it was on Moraine Dome that the conviction first grew upon me that there are two distinct moraine series in the Sierra Nevada, recording two glacial episodes separated from each other by a long interval of time. The story of Moraine Dome, as told, is not really complete, as I intended it to be "popular" and as nearly free from complications as possible. It does not, however, omit any important facts. Reference might have been made to the older moraines shown on the map, which are so dim as to be unrecognizable as topographic features and can be traced only as belts containing Cathedral granite and other rock material foreign to the Yosemite neighborhood. Perched erratics occur on the Quarter Domes which lie just under the upper limit reached by the earlier ice. These domes show residual masses of granite decaying in place some five feet high.

Dr. [Grove Karl] Gilbert is familiar with Moraine Dome and has visited it twice. The photo of the aplite wall was taken by him. Evidently his conclusions agree with mine, to judge from the notes appended to his photos in the Survey collection. Neither of us, however, knew that the other had visited Moraine Dome until I showed him my views (in 1906 it was, I believe).

I should greatly appreciate criticism from you.

[Unsigned]

---

[1] Draft of a letter presumably sent to A. C. Lawson, and attached to the unpublished manuscript entitled "Little Studies in the Yosemite Region, V. The Story of Moraine Dome."

As to the real nature of the embankment, there never was a moment's doubt; it was manifestly a "moraine" of the ancient Merced Glacier, a ridge of ice-transported rock debris, deposited along the margin of the "mer-de-glace" that once filled the Little Yosemite. Its very shape, together with the character of

General view of north side of Little Yosemite Valley. Moraine Dome in the center, marked by a cross. The great morainal embankment is accentuated by a row of dots. In the background is Clouds Rest. The faint, white horizontal line to the right of Moraine Dome is the boulder-studded crest of the highest moraine of the later ice flood. The earlier ice flood overtopped most of the low mountains along the sky line.

the boulders and cobbles protruding from its surface, many of them rounded and polished, and some representing rock types foreign to the Yosemite neighborhood, at once established its identity.

Moraines are plentiful about the Yosemite Valley and its branches, but none had been observed so remarkably clean cut and perfect, nor had any been found in so striking a position, wreathed, as it were, about a dome. And so, quite naturally, the appropriateness suggested itself of naming the eminence for the embankment—and then and there the height was christened Moraine Dome.

A full appreciation of the significance of the embankment, however, was not

gained until afterwards. As the locality became better known in the course of
the survey, the fact developed that the embankment on the side of the dome is
the highest and largest of a series of parallel moraines. Spaced at intervals of
a few hundred feet across the rounding granite slope below the great embankment are a number of such glacial deposits, all describing sympathetic arcs, all
slanting westward at approximately the same rate. Each evidently records a
halt in the subsidence of the ice flood, or a transitory rise of its lowering surface;
together they tell the story of the progressively diminishing pulsations of the
glacier during its decline. Some consist of little more than a mere row of boulders
from among which the finer material has washed away; they bespeak fluctuations of ephemeral briefness. Others have the form of massive ridges, ten to
fifteen feet high and supporting dense growths of manzanita and occasional
pines; these attest rises of relatively long duration.

However, one must guard against interpreting these features with too much
confidence; moraines are inherently tricky in their nature, changing deceptively
in aspect from place to place. Thus, the great upper embankment on Moraine
Dome, by its superior size and bulk, might readily lead one to infer that the
maximum stage of the ice flood was an unusually protracted one; but, when

Looking up the crest of the winding embankment. The summit of Moraine Dome lies to the left.

this embankment is followed westward to the base of the dome, it is found to divide into two discrete moraine bodies which thence accompany each other as sister ridges 200 to 300 feet apart. Still farther west, upon entering the great embayment in the north side of the Little Yosemite Valley, each of these two ridges again is found to split into three separate sharp crests. What on the dome, therefore, would be taken for a single, compact, heavy moraine, proves in reality to be a composite mass, containing the proceeds of six separate glacier fluctuations.

The cause of this mysterious behavior of the moraines is to be sought in the influence exerted on the shape of the ice stream by the variations in the width of the valley trough. Opposite Moraine Dome there is a marked narrowing between promontories of sharp declivity. There the lesser fluctuations in the glacier's volume found expression in only insignificant lateral oscillations of its borders, and the moraines, in consequence, lie plastered against and upon each other, in places indistinguishably merged together. But farther west there is a pronounced widening of the valley trough, accompanied by gentler side slopes, and there, naturally, the borders of the ice stream expanded and contracted in obedience to volume changes on a relatively generous scale, placing each moraine an

The great morainal embankment viewed from the bare granite slope of Moraine Dome above

appreciable distance from its fellows. Particularly complete and detailed, for this reason, is the morainal record in the great embayment on the north side, as the traveler on the Sunrise Trail may conveniently observe. That route, in the first 1000 feet of its ascent from the floor of the Little Yosemite Valley, traverses 30 moraines in succession.

Let us now see whether it is possible to trace the course of the upper embankment eastward from the dome. As was stated, the embankment terminates at a point about 150 feet below the summit. It stops there, however, not because the glacier was deficient in rock debris east of this point, but because the precipitous character of the cliffs here does not permit the lodgment of loose debris. It may reasonably be anticipated, therefore, that farther east, on more favorable ground, the moraine will be found to resume its course. And, so, indeed, it does; only, one must not look for any plain sailing in a search of this kind. The windings of a moraine are in considerable measure conditioned by the features of the landscape, and, in a locality of peculiar configuration such as this, are likely to be devious and elusive, like the turns and twists in a rabbit's track.

Moraine Dome, it will be observed on the map, does not curve down symmetrically in all directions. Northeastward it is prolonged in a nearly level, round-backed ridge, half a mile long and only some 60 feet lower than the summit. At its farther extremity this ridge carries a knoll of about the same height as the dome. Somewhere on this ridge, to judge from the slant of the embankment on the dome, the upper moraines may be expected to be found again. Starting out in search along the back bone, however, one is disappointed to find it bare and smooth like the dome itself. Even the lowest sag, which would naturally seem to hold most promise, is utterly devoid of debris. But on the terminal knoll, in the place where one would least expect to find them, there the moraines turn up again. At first they impress one as a confused jumble of boulder heaps, partly overgrown with brush; but a little study shows them to consist of several distinct bands, looped over the summit at intervals and trailing down to the southwest and to the northwest at a strong angle with the slope.

On the south side of the knoll the loops are cut off short by the same great cliff that interrupts the embankment on the dome, but on the north side they can be traced down all the way to Sunrise Creek, across the Sunrise Trail and up again through a long arc to the south base of Clouds Rest.

On the ground the significance of this arc is not readily apparent, as the forest growth precludes a comprehensive view; but when seen in its entirety on the map the arc is at once recognized as the outline of a short lobe of the Merced Glacier. That ice stream, it would appear, split upon the knoll and sent a small portion of its mass through the saddle to the north. How near the glacier came to overtopping the height is attested by the looped position of the moraines. The most advanced of the series even lies a little west of the highest point of the knoll. One wonders that the ice, having come this far, did not engulf the low ridge before it and advance to Moraine Dome; but its viscosity evidently did not permit this.

Moraine Dome, together with the ridge extending northeastward from it, is, then, of special interest as a landmark demarcating what appears to be the highest level reached by the ice in the Little Yosemite Valley. Should any-one doubt the correctness of this interpretation, let him pursue the moraines described farther east. He will find them running along the north side of the valley as far as Sunrise Mountain, in the form of a great series of massive, parallel embankments. The Sunrise Trail for a considerable distance takes advantage of the mile-long, uninterrupted stretches of good going which these embankments afford and at last surmounts the highest of the series.

No one, not even the most casual of observers can help noticing the upper-most moraine as he crosses it. Like an artificial battlement it looms, crowned with gigantic granite boulders that produce a white line through the forest visible from afar (photo, page 65). Below it are tiers of successively lower crests, all rock studded, and imparting to the mountain side a chaotic, wild appearance. Above, on the other hand, the slope is relatively smooth and featureless, smoth-ered for the most part under a heavy mantle of disintegrated granite sand. So striking is the contrast, indeed, so conspicuous is the boundary between the moraine littered slope below and the smooth slope above that no one fully cog-nizant of its significance but will unhesitatingly declare: This line marks the highest level of the ice flood. Above it the glacier never rose.

And yet again, it is well not to be too positive about these matters.

On continuing the ascent of Moraine Dome from the upper end of the em-bankment, what does one find? About 30 feet below the summit, on the south side, is an elongated boulder measuring 12 by 6 by 5 feet, perched on a pedestal some three feet high (photo, page 70). The pedestal is made up of remnants of inclined shells clearly belonging to the dome (surface shells of this kind, it may be explained in passing, are now recognized to be a normal feature of the Sierra domes), but the great capping boulder consists of a material differing conspicuously from the local rock. Moraine Dome is composed of a fairly even-textured granite of creamy color speckled with dark mineral (Half Dome granite it is called by geologists, as Half Dome consists of this rock), while the perched boulder is of a pinkish granite with swarms of large, square-cornered feldspar crystals of a paler hue. More resistant to weathering than the matrix between them, these crystals stand out on the surface in high relief, like so many domino blocks, two to three inches long, lending the rock a perculiar, lumpy aspect.

The "erratic" boulder of Cathedral granite on its pedestal. The rock is 12 feet long and 5 feet high. It attests a much earlier and higher ice flood than the morainal embankments farther down.

Nowhere in the Yosemite region is this type of granite found "in place"; but higher up in the Sierra Nevada it constitutes the prevailing country rock over large areas, notably in the upper Tuolumne basin. The rugged chain which terminates in Cathedral Peak is largely composed of it, and, accordingly, the rock has been named Cathedral granite.

The nearest locality from which the boulder could have been derived is Long Meadow, which lies back of Sunrise Mountain, some five miles to the northeast. Clearly there is but one agent that could have brought it from that place, and that is a glacier. The very size of the boulder precludes the possibility of its having been transported by another agent. Besides, it is known that the

Merced Glacier carried considerable of this material, fragments being plentiful in all of the moraines described.

The glacial origin of the boulder being admitted, the conclusion previously reached that the great embankment on the flank of the dome marks the highest level reached by the ice, must be revised. Evidently the glacier did rise higher once.

But, it may be objected, is this one boulder the sole evidence available of a higher ice stage? Granted that it is a sure-enough "erratic," one would feel better satisfied, were there additional testimony of some sort. Such testimony indeed is found in the presence of another boulder of Cathedral granite, located on the very summit of the dome. Its position is such as to suggest that the entire dome may once have been overridden by the ice, and that, in order to determine the highest level attained by the glacier, the search may have to be carried to higher ground. This, it should be said, has actually been done, with the result that the ice is now definitely known to have overtopped the dome by five hundred feet at least.

In the meanwhile the entire story of Moraine Dome is not told. In the first place, there is a certain significance in the almost complete isolation of the two erratics mentioned. Search as one may, there is not another rock of extraneous origin to be found on the dome. Yet the summit is broad and level, affording ample space for a heavy glacial deposit. If moraines are able to maintain themselves in the form of strong embankments on the steeply inclined flanks of the dome, why should there be such a paucity of glacial material on the much more favorable, level summit?

The suspicion here insinuates itself that possibly one has to do here with the vestiges of what may once have been a moraine of considerable volume,— a moraine, however, of a very much earlier ice flood than the one whose history is so fully recorded in the heavy embankments lower down, a moraine so ancient, indeed, that all of its material has by this time disintegrated and washed away, save for these two solitary erratics. Several things seem to strengthen this suspicion. For one thing, both rocks have long since lost their ice-smoothed, rounded contour, and have weathered down to irregular, lumpy forms. Again, both rocks have pedestals. That the smaller one on the summit possesses such a support, has not been mentioned. The fact is that it no longer occupies its pedestal, but leans against the base, having slipped down apparently not long ago. That the little pile, which stands about twelve inches high, really once did serve as a support for the erratic, however, is beyond question; the badly decomposed granite of the pedestal clearly could not have survived above the general surface of the dome, save through the presence of a protecting cover of some sort. Indeed, there is no doubt but what the pedestals of both boulders owe their preservation to the protective influence of the resistant cap rocks. They have remained standing while the surrounding parts of the dome have gradually wasted away under the attacks of the elements. They point, therefore, to a general denudation of the dome that has been in progress for a considerable lapse of time. The exact rate at which the surface of a granite dome is annually lowered is, of course, not definitely known, but it is safe to say that the period involved was a lengthy one, to be reckoned in thousands of years.

Perched erratics, it is to be noted, are by no means a common feature of the Yosemite region. Below the great morainal embankment that was thought to mark the culmination of the ice tide, perched boulders are signally absent. Detached erratics abound between the moraine ridges, it is true, but invariably they are found resting on the hard, smooth surface of the granite, which, even as the boulders themselves, appears to have undergone little or no change since the withdrawal of the ice, and in many places still retains the polish and scourings, imparted to it by the grinding glacier. Similarly among the thousands and thousands of glacial boulders scattered over those wonderful expanses of ice-smoothed, bare granite which one traverses on the way to Merced Lake, there is not one to be found supported by a residual pedestal. So striking is this fact after one has become acquainted with the conditions on the summit of Moraine Dome, that one cannot escape concluding that the contrast betokens a great difference in age between the glacial material lying respectively above and below the line of the great embankment. That embankment accordingly assumes a new and more definite significance; it appears to mark the culminating stage of a relatively recent ice flood, whereas the ancient-looking perched erratics on the dome attest a glacial epoch of a relatively remote date.

It may have been remarked that the pedestals of the two erratics on Moraine Dome do not accord in height. That of the large lower boulder is three feet tall, while that of the smaller rock on the summit measures only about one foot. Too much significance should not be attached to this disparity, for there is good reason to believe that neither boulder has retained its exact position throughout the entire period of its lodgment on the dome. The lower one, being situated on a steep incline, no doubt has crept down hill from time to time, as its disintegrating support crumbled under the load, or as its equilibrium shifted through the flaking off of portions of its own mass. Indeed the aspect of the pedestal is such as to warrant the inference that the great erratic has not lain long in its present position.

As for the boulder on the summit, the chances are that in slipping from its support, it has merely repeated an act it has performed before. A rock of such moderate dimensions (it measures but little over three feet across) is not likely to generate a pedestal of any considerable height. The supporting column,

The little "aplite" wall near the umbrella tree on the summit of Moraine Dome. Its height, 7 feet, affords a rough measure of the depth to which the dome has been denuded since the passage of the earlier ice flood.

because of its small diameter, would soon be weathered through and through, and would either crumble down or shed the cap rock. The latter, in its new position on the surface of the dome, would then through its protective influence, proceed to generate another pedestal, and this column, in time, would probably fare like the first. Thus, it will be seen, the erratic may have occupied several low pedestals in succession.

These conjectures may seem far fetched perhaps, nevertheless they possess strong elements of probability, as is indicated by certain other residual features on Moraine Dome. Scarcely 50 feet to the northeast of the small erratic on the summit, close to a dead umbrella tree that marks the highest point, is what might be taken for a dilapidated garden wall, built of dry slabs, with many chinks that let through the daylight. It is 7 feet high and 4 feet thick (see above), and over a length of about 12 feet seems entire, but the southern end appears to have tumbled down in part, and terminates in shapeless piles of slabs.

The interpretation of this odd feature is not difficult. It is a portion of a thick vein or "dike" of a yellow, fine-grained igneous rock, known as aplite, that cuts vertically through the body of the dome. Aplite, it should be explained, weathers much more slowly than does granite. As the surface of the dome, therefore, was being lowered by the gradual wasting away of the granite, the dike came to stand out more and more, attaining at last its present wall-like aspect. The surrounding granite is still disintegrating and wasting away, and as a consequence the wall is even now growing imperceptibly in height.

The weather, however, has also told on the aplite, and has greatly weakened the little structure. It has caused the slabs (which are remnants of surface shells that once extended over the entire crown of the dome) to crack in places, and has enlarged the partings between them to gaping holes and chinks. In fact, the greater part of the wall, as stated, has already broken down, probably under the stress of the heavy winter snows.

Special interest attaches to the best preserved and highest portion of the wall, as its height affords perhaps the most trustworthy index available of the depth to which Moraine Dome has been stripped since the passage of the earlier ice flood.

In the first place there is no possibility that the wall might in part have been inherited from a time antedating the earlier ice flood. An obstacle so feeble, standing at right angles to the current of the ice stream, would inevitably have been completely razed. Whoever has traveled through the High Sierra may have noted that on the great expanses of ice-polished granite characteristic of that region, all aplite dikes, the largest as well as the smallest, are shorn level with the surrounding granite. There is thus every reason to believe that the aplite dike on Moraine Dome was similarly smoothed off by the overriding glacier, and did not begin to weather out until after the culmination of the earlier ice flood.

No trace of glacier polish remains on the top of the wall today (which is not surprising, as all polish of the earlier ice flood has long since vanished throughout the Yosemite region, except in those rare localities where it was fortuitously preserved under debris that has remained undisturbed by the later ice), and thus there is no guarantee that the top coincides even roughly with the original glaciated surface. Nevertheless, it seems safe to say that the wall has not been reduced much below the initial level—not as much as a foot, perhaps,—for its top is broad and flat so that superincumbent slabs (if ever there were any) could not readily have fallen from it without leaving behind a fragment. Nor are there any broken slabs about the base of the wall that appear to have been derived from the top.

Again, there is a remarkable accordance in height between this aplite wall and two other walls of a similar kind, located near the southwestern end of the summit of the dome. These walls also owe their existence to the superior resisting power of aplite, but they differ from the little wall described in that the aplite veins in them are steeply inclined instead of vertical, and form slanting roofs under which masses of granite have remained preserved. They are therefore composite bodies, containing both granite and aplite, and are rather massive and irregular in shape. The upper wall is 8 feet high, about the same as the wall near the umbrella tree; the lower is almost 11 feet high, but, as it is situated on a steep south-facing slope where denudation is bound to progress more rapidly than on a level tract, one should properly expect it to be taller than either of the walls standing on the summit platform. There is thus substantial agreement in the height of the three walls on Moraine Dome, although they are somewhat dissimilar in make-up and of unequal thickness, and accordingly one feels justified in accepting 8 feet as a minimum measure of the thickness of granite that has been stripped from the summit of the dome since the culmination of the earlier ice flood. Small wonder that the morainal material attesting that ice flood is so scarce on Moraine Dome! Indeed, one marvels, in the light of these evidences of wholesale weathering, that even the two erratics of Cathedral granite have remained to tell the tale.

The story that Moraine Dome tells is then, briefly, a story of two glacial epochs, separated by a lengthy interval of time.[2] The earlier ice flood was by far the mightier and rose to considerably higher levels than the later one, but so remote was the date of its occurrence that since then Moraine Dome and probably all similar granite heights in the Yosemite region have lost at least 8 feet in height, and the morainal material that was deposited on them has all but disappeared. On the other hand, the later ice flood culminated so recently, relatively speaking, that the scoured granite surfaces left by it appear even now essentially unchanged, and retain their polish over large areas, while the fluctuations of the declining glacier are still fully recorded in great series of moraines, many of which are strong even on exposed places such as the slopes of domes.

[2] Later, at least three and possibly four epochs were recognized. See pp. 114, 156.—ED.

Time was when the question at issue was whether the Yosemite had ever been visited by ice or not. Now that question is not only definitely settled, but one can speak with confidence of two separate glacial episodes. And, in view of the strong denudation that appears to have taken place since the earlier of these epochs, and has so greatly dimmed its record, one feels justified in going one step further and in asking whether there may not have been other, still earlier ice floods whose traces by now are completely effaced?

It is not known with certainty why this manuscript remained unpublished, though probably it was because of the many urgent duties which Matthes as a member of the Geological Survey had to assume in the critical world situation prior to World War I. However, a technical abstract, "Moraine Dome and the Moraines of the Little Yosemite Valley," was published in the Journal of the Washington Academy of Sciences, *volume 4 (1914), pages 295–296. Also, Matthes' interpretations were set forth in Professional Paper 160 (1930), though differently stated in that volume.*—ED.

Matthes Crest, Yosemite National Park. By Reid Moran

COCKSCOMB

CREST

FAMILIAR to all who have visited the Tuolumne Meadows, and transcending perhaps all other mountain groups overlooking that campers' paradise in spectacular beauty and monumental dignity, are the pinnacled and spired peaks of Unicorn, Echo, and Cathedral. Each has its own individuality, striking and unforgettable, each is wholly different from the others, yet all are notably alike in one respect: their frail minarets and splintered crests stand planted upon full-bodied mountains of great bulk, all rising to approximately the same height; they seem like delicate super-structures, specially added for the sake of ornamentation. Indeed, they recall the slender turrets and spires on certain ponderous cathedrals of Old Europe.

The significance of this peculiar style of mountain architecture, which is not prevalent in the Sierra Nevada, has been hinted at by more than one writer. Muir and Chase both have suggested that the sharp pinnacles and crests may be summits that were never overridden by the ice of the Glacial Epoch; that stood out above even the highest ice-floods and escaped being planed down and rounded off as were the massive shoulders of the mountain pedestals under them. This explanation, though only conjectural, was eminently reasonable, and it is a genuine satisfaction, now that the region has been submitted to a systematic and detailed study, to be able to confirm its correctness and to corroborate with positive and abundant evidence the surmise of these two keen and perceptive observers.

However, the matter is not so simple as it at first may seem. In Muir's day glacial science was in its infancy, and no man had as yet that perspective of the succession of ice-ages and intervening epochs of milder climate which the world-wide research of the last two decades has made known to us. To Muir and his contemporaries the Glacial Epoch still seemed a single, uninterrupted cycle of glacial conditions that slowly reached a climax, like an oncoming tide, and then slowly waned, the glaciers making many repeated but progressively feebler re-advances, like the waves of an out-going tide. Today we know that the Glacial Epoch, so-called, really consisted of several prolonged ice-tides separated by equally prolonged intervals, during each of which the continental ice-sheet and the lesser ice-bodies on our western mountain ranges shrank back to their sources and perhaps vanished altogether.

In the Sierra Nevada indications of at least two great ice-floods have been clearly recognized by several observers—two ice-floods that occurred manifestly at widely different times, the later culminating probably only twenty thousand years ago, the earlier, perhaps as much as several hundred thousand years ago.[1] The evidence is the more readily established as the later ice-flood was the smaller and less extensive of the two and left undisturbed the moraines—that is, the ridges of ice-carried rock debris—that mark the limits of the earlier ice-flood. In no part of the Sierra Nevada have these facts been ascertained with more precision than in the Yosemite region and the High Sierra immediately above it. Thus it is now definitely known that the later ice-flood invaded the Yosemite Valley only as far as the Bridalveil Meadows, whereas the earlier ice-flood advanced eleven miles farther down the Merced Canyon, coming to a halt a short distance beyond El Portal.

It will be clear from this that there must be from the Bridalveil Meadows upward throughout the Yosemite region and adjoining the High Sierra not one but two "ice-lines," each marking the culmination of an ice-flood. The pursuit of these two ice-lines up towards the crest of the range was, indeed, for the better part of two seasons the writer's most engrossing occupation. He traced them in detail and mapped them along the length of the Yosemite, up through the Little Yosemite and the upper Merced Basin and all its tributary canyons, and also up through Tenaya Canyon and the great Tuolumne Basin and its tributary canyons. The result, it may be said, was to him, as glacialist, a genuine surprise. The two ice-lines, which in the lower Yosemite lie several thousand feet apart in altitude, were found to approach each other as they ascend the range and ultimately to coalesce at its crest. One might reasonably have expected the extensive and deep ice-fields and glaciers of the earlier epoch to have come from a Sierra crest completely domed over with smoothly sloping, unbroken

[1] See footnotes on pages 114 and 156.—ED.

snow-fields, and the relatively modest ice-stream of the later epoch to have flowed forth from cirques filled only to moderate depth, and partitioned from one another by bare rock crests and "arêtes" rising high above the ice; but, curiously, it appears that the snow conditions along the Sierra crest were substantially the same in both epochs. *The snows that fed the vast glaciers of the earlier epoch filled the summit cirques to no greater depth than did the snows that formed the smaller glaciers of the later epoch.* The significance of this remarkable coincidence need not be here discussed—it would lead too far afield; suffice it for our purpose that the fact has been established.

A few figures will help to give more definiteness to one's conception of the relation of the two ice-lines. The later Yosemite Glacier ended at the Bridalveil Meadows at an altitude of 3900 feet, but the lateral moraines left by the earlier ice-stream on either side of the Yosemite chasm lie 2700 feet above this spot. At the head of the valley the later glacier attained a depth of about 1500 feet, but the lateral moraines of the earlier glacier still lie 2400 feet higher. Within the next few miles the two ice-lines converge with remarkable rapidity. In the Little Yosemite, for instance, they are only 600 feet apart. There the later ice rose within 100 feet of the top of Moraine Dome, but the earlier ice passed over it with a depth of over 500 feet. Opposite Lake Merced the difference in altitude between the two ice-lines dwindles to 400 feet, and thence upward, to the ultimate source of the glacier under Mount Lyell, the difference steadily decreases until it becomes a vanishing quantity.

Following the ice-lines up through Tenaya Canyon, they are found to be 2100 feet apart in altitude opposite Half Dome. That rock monument was engulfed by the earlier ice up to within 700 feet of its summit, but even the foot of its great cliff rose 800 feet above the surface of the later glacier. At the head of Tenaya Canyon the earlier ice rose only 900 feet higher than the later ice, and still farther up, on the divide between the Tenaya and Tuolumne basins, the two ice-lines are only 400 feet apart. In the great upper Tuolumne Basin, which held an ice-field embracing 140 square miles, the earlier and later ice-floods differed only 200 feet in level, as is to be inferred from the two ice-lines on Ragged Peak. And on the Cathedral Range, which was in large measure the generator of this immense ice-field, being the great hedge behind which the wind-blown snows accumulated, the difference was least of all. From Cathedral Peak eastward to Mount Lyell it lessened by degrees until at length it became insignificant.

The figures are but a very few out of many scores determined by the writer on both ice-lines. Indeed, the total number of determinations made was large enough to enable him to construct a contour map of each ice surface. These contour maps, he is happy to say, have furnished excellent proof of the mutual concordance and consistency of the data.

The group of pinnacled mountains, it will be clear from the foregoing, stands in a region where the two ice-floods reached substantially the same height. Most of the work of paring away the sides of the pinnacles and crests was done by the earlier ice-flood, which was the one of greater duration, but the later ice-flood undoubtedly did much to accentuate the effect produced by the first. It is a significant fact that farther down on the Sierra flank, where the ice-lines diverge widely in altitude, and where the fluctuations in level of each of the floods no doubt were of considerable amplitude, no attenuated pinnacles or crests rising abruptly from ice-rounded mountains are to be found.

In Greenland, which is one of the few parts of the earth even now under the dominion of the ice, an Ekimo word is commonly used to designate those barren rocky summits that protrude here and there above the rapidly descending glaciers forming the fringes of the vast and otherwise continual glacial mantle. That word is *nunatak*. Physiographers throughout the world have adopted it as a technical term for rocky summits rising above surrounding ice-sheets and glaciers. The pinnacles and crests of the Cathedral Range might, therefore, be referred to as *former nunataks*. But the appropriateness and desirability of so styling them are, in the writer's opinion, open to question.

For one thing, it must be borne in mind that the pinnacles and crest were not the only summits of the Cathedral Range, nor of the entire High Sierra, that remained uncovered by the ice. There were many larger and more massive summits of varying shapes and designs, and even occasional plateau-like tracts. Only half a mile to the southwest of Unicorn Peak, for instance, stands a massive peak of blunted, pyramidal form (still unnamed, although higher than Unicorn) that rose several hundred feet above the ice. Parsons Peak and the broad-topped mountain (still unnamed) northeast of Vogelsang Pass are examples of elevated plateaus that remained emergent. Surely no one would think of placing these in the same class with the attenuated crest of Unicorn Peak, the triangular teeth of Echo Peak, or the ethereal spires of the Cathedral. "Former nunatak" might do in a generic and vague sense for all of them, but there is clearly need of a distinctive term for the more fragile, evanescent forms.

Cockscomb Crest, the most magnificent of all the sharply attenuated crests that indicate the highest level reached by the ice in the High Sierra. By François Matthes

What is more, there is need, it seems to the writer, of a term from the Sierra Nevada itself, if possible from the locality where the type is found in its purest form.

Now, as a matter of fact, neither Unicorn, Echo, nor Cathedral represents a "pure type" of mountain sculpture. In each the paring effect of the ice is somewhat obscured or even outweighed by other influences, either by the headward gnawing of local cirque glaciers or by peculiarities of the structure of the rock. When closely analyzed each is found to present a rather complex case. But fortunately there are in the same neighborhood three other peaks or crests each of which might well be taken as a type example.

The first of these is that narrow, linear, bladelike crest southwest of the Cathedral Pass and overlooking Long Meadow, which has been aptly named Columbia's Finger. On the topographic map the name is misplaced, and as a consequence there has arisen some confusion as to the identity of the feature to which it is supposed to refer. The writer himself is willing to admit some uncertainty on his own part, but, if form be the main criterion—and it certainly should be in a case of this sort—then the name surely belongs to the crest just mentioned. For that crest terminates southward in a tall, columnar rock pinnacle that seems to point heavenward like a slender, tapering finger. It is especially impressive when viewed endwise, from the direction of Long Meadow, and doubtless it was named by someone who traveled through that flat on his way to Soda Springs. The case is parallel to that of Unicorn Peak, which was named unquestionably by someone in the Tuolumne Meadows, and whose crest does not resemble a pointing horn except when viewed endwise, from one particular direction.

The second crest in question rises a scant mile to the north of Columbia's Finger, and is of exactly the same narrow, linear type. It even duplicates the latter's terminal pinnacle, but only in what, by contrast, might be called a "stubby thumb." More perfectly modeled even than Columbia's Finger, this crest eloquently tells its story—one wonders that it should still be without a name.

The third crest is a much more imposing feature than either of the foregoing. Rising abruptly from a long-drawn ridge as even-topped as the roof of a house, about a mile south of the Unicorn, it attracts the eye at once by its wonderful symmetry and the supreme boldness of its design. Seen endwise it seems but a narrow blade, springing almost without transition from the broad mountain

under it. From certain directions it is suggestive of the upper half of an orna-
mental "fleur-de-lis," but from most view points it resembles nothing so much
as a splendidly sculptured, gigantic cockscomb. Indeed, it stands planted upon
the ice-smoothed ridge as a cockscomb surmounts the proud head of a cock.

The appropriateness of the name Cockscomb may be judged from the photograph on page 81. The writer does not claim to be a connoisseur in poultry;
nevertheless, he believes that the likeness to a lobate cockscomb is fairly close—
as close as one might expect to find in a piece of mountain sculpture.

Last summer it was the writer's pleasure to accompany a party from the
Sierra Club under the leadership of Mr. Colby across the Cathedral Range by
the natural pass above Elizabeth Lake, and into the country at the headwaters
of Echo Creek, where the Cockscomb stands. He took that occasion tentatively
to submit to those present the name Cockscomb, and was gratified to find it meet
with general approval. And so, with additional confidence, he now submits it to
the entire membership.[2]

There is a special advantage in the adoption of the name that is worth
pointing out. Not only is the appellation Cockscomb apt because it is descriptive
of the form of this crest, but it would also be an extremely convenient generic
term for the designation of all similarly sculptured crests—of all crests such
as those previously described, which owe their attentuated linear forms to the
paring action of the ice that split upon them and passed on either side without
overwhelming them. It would admirably serve the physiographer's needs as
standing for the type of mountain sculpture of which the beautiful crest under
discussion is the finest example known.

In conclusion, a word anent the desirability, the urgency even, of the members of the Sierra Club giving serious thought to the bestowal of appropriate
names upon those peaks, lakes, and other prominent landmarks within the
Yosemite National Park which are as yet unnamed. The next few years doubtless will see a tremendous influx of tourists and pleasure-seekers into the higher
portions of the park, more especially into the Tuolumne Meadows and the Lake
Merced neighborhood. That influx, indeed, has already set in, as all those of
us who camped with the Sierra Club at Soda Springs last summer have had ample
opportunity to see for ourselves. One inevitable result will be the proposal of
names for all such features of the landscape as are of especial popular interest

[2] The name "Cockscomb Crest" now appears on the topographic map of Yosemite National
Park.—ED.

and still without names on the map. That this naming is likely to be mostly haphazard and ill-considered is almost a foregone conclusion—one need but visit a tourist resort where the naming has been left largely to the public and the guides. We of the Sierra Club, it seems to the writer, owe it to the glorious mountain country that is so dear to us to forestall such a fate for its landmarks. As it is, some of them already bear names that are distinctly inappropriate or even objectionable.

The writer ventures to make this suggestion, although he is by no means certain that Cockscomb Crest, the name proposed by him, will stand. It is still to be acted upon, first by the Sierra Club as a whole, and second by the United States Geographic Board. But he cherishes the hope that in any event his proposal will stimulate interest in the duty before us—and it is plainly a duty—of finding suitable names for the features of the High Sierra.

Reprinted from Sierra Club Bulletin, *January, 1920, pages 21–28.*

KINGS RIVER CANYON
AND YOSEMITE VALLEY

IT IS NOT without some hesitation that the writer ventures upon this theme. For he is mindful of the truth there is in that well-known saying about comparisons. Nor would he essay any comparison of the Kings River Canyon and the Yosemite Valley as two masterpieces of nature's handiwork. That is a task for a more gifted pen than his. Besides, there is no need for it has been done, and well done, by acknowledged masters. What he proposes to give in these pages is a comparison of the outstanding features and characteristics of the two chasms as a geologist understands them.

Perhaps it should be added, as a geologist *of the present day* understands them, for we have now at our disposal a wholly new branch of earth science, a branch that has developed almost entirely since the eighties of the last century —geomorphology, the science of the evolution of mountains and valleys and the surface features of the earth in general. Its application to the Sierra Nevada already has yielded a veritable harvest of new knowledge; it has given us an insight such as was impossible heretofore of that range—not only during the Ice Age and since its close, but also during the long stretches of time that went before. The Yosemite Valley has been studied in particularly close detail, and as a result we can now trace its evolution back through successive stages all the way to its beginning in a remote geologic period. The Kings River Canyon, it is true, has been accorded thus far little more than a reconnaissance, yet the salient facts of its history now also stand revealed, the key to them being furnished by the research that has been done in the Yosemite region and in other parts of the Sierra Nevada. What is to follow here, then, is an interpretation of the resemblances and differences between the two chasms in the light of this new knowledge.

First, let us see what the main points of resemblance and difference are. As
is generally agreed by those familiar with both chasms, the Yosemite Valley
and the Kings River Canyon[1] are most closely similar in their larger modeling,
less so in their detail sculpture, and least in their environmental setting. Both are
hewn like gigantic troughs, steep-sided, level-floored, and remarkably constant
in width throughout, although more or less sinuous in course. In cross-sections
they are broadly U-shaped, in contrast to the other great canyons of the lower
Sierra, which are prevailingly V-shaped. They are even more broadly U-shaped
than the typical glacier troughs of the High Sierra, which are among the most
perfectly modeled of their kind.

Indeed, it may well be said that their broad, level floors, which beckon to
us with their charming sunlit groves and the sublime vistas of cliff and peak

[1] Here is meant, of course, that broad-floored stretch of the South Fork canyon which extends
from the mouth of Bubbs Creek westward to Cedar Grove—the "Kings River Yosemite" of John
Muir. (See U.S.G.S. topographic map of Tehipite Quadrangle.)

A view down Yosemite Valley from the trail above Union Point showing the broad U-shape of
the chasm. Sentinel Rock, Cathedral Rocks, and El Capitan. By Ansel Adams

which they afford, largely make these yosemites what they are to us and what no narrow-bottomed gorge, however profound, can be.

Both the Yosemite Valley and Kings River Canyon, be it observed further, are limited in extent strictly by their floors. At the lower end each narrows down to an essentially V-shaped canyon, no wider at the bottom than the channel of the river (Fig. 3). And at the head each branches abruptly into two lesser canyons—or, to put it differently, each chasm commences abruptly on a grand scale of its own, the branch canyons opening into it by separate portals and at different levels. And so the Yosemite and the Kings River canyons both have the appearance of being complete in themselves, set off from the canyons above and below, although in reality they are but short links in extensive canyon systems.

Upon closer inspection, nevertheless, the Yosemite Valley and the Kings River Canyon are found to differ appreciably in their proportions—their ratios of length, width, and depth. The Yosemite Valley is seven miles long, on an

A similar view down the Kings River Canyon showing its pronounced Yosemite-like character. By J. N. LeConte

average three-fourths of a mile wide from cliff base to cliff base, and two miles wide from brink to brink; and it has a depth of 3000 to 3500 feet from brink to floor. The Kings River Canyon, on the other hand, is nine miles long, on an average only about three-eighths of a mile wide from cliff base to cliff base, and but slightly over one mile wide from brink to brink, in so far as it can be said to have any brinks. Its depth below the same ill-defined brinks ranges from 2000 to 2500 feet. The Kings River Canyon, therefore, though two miles longer than the Yosemite, is only one-half as wide and two-thirds as deep.

The cliffs in both chasms are distinguished in general by the same massive, monumental style of sculpture; but a comparison of individual rock-forms must naturally result in favor of the Yosemite. Nor is this because of any real deficiency in such forms in the Kings River Canyon, but rather because of the matchless wealth and variety with which the Yosemite is endowed. No other chasm on this continent, nor perhaps on any continent, possesses within so small a compass so remarkable an assemblage of uniquely sculptured cliffs and monuments.

The upper part of the Kings River Canyon, however, is no distant rival; its Grand Sentinel and North Dome, though not quite so clean-cut as comparable forms in the Yosemite, are fully as majestic and impressive; and the Sphinx, were it situated in the tourist-thronged and well-advertised Yosemite region, no doubt would have long since become known the world over as one of its striking landmarks. But the lower part of the canyon possesses few sculptures of equal distinction. Some of its cliffs are of noble proportions, but they are not of the kind that stand out in the memory forever.

In another respect also, it must be admitted, the Kings River Canyon cannot compete with the Yosemite—namely, in wealth of waterfalls. It possesses really but one cataract of note, that of Roaring River; and that cataract is to be measured only in tens of feet, whereas the falls in the Yosemite Valley are measured in hundreds of feet.

This lack of falling waters in the Kings River Canyon is of peculiar interest, in that it is due in large part to the scarcity of typical "hanging valleys"—that is, tributary valleys opening abruptly at a considerable height above the floor of the main chasm. In the Yosemite region "hanging valleys" notably abound. Typical examples are the valley of Yosemite Creek, which opens at a height of 2565 feet; the valley of Ribbon Creek, which opens at a height of over 3000 feet; and the valley of Illilouette Creek, which opens at a height of about 1800 feet. From their mouths leap the glorious waterfalls for which the Yosemite is famed. The streams tributary to the Kings River Canyon, on the contrary, have nearly all cut their valleys down to so great depth that they debouch at or but slightly above the level of its floor.

True hanging valleys, nevertheless, are not wholly wanting in the Kings River region: the valley of Bubbs Creek, for instance, opens at a height of fully

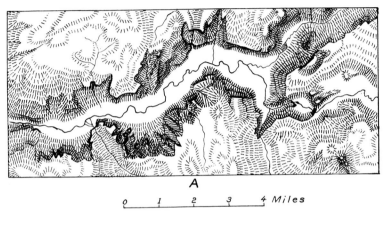

A

0   1   2   3   4 *Miles*

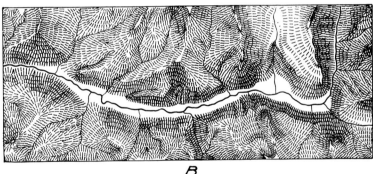

B

Figure 3.—Hachure maps of Yosemite Valley (A) and Kings River Canyon (B), permitting a direct comparison of their main features (same scale).

1400 feet; the valley of Copper Creek, at a height of 2000 feet; and the valley of Granite Creek, at a height of at least 1200 feet. But their streams, instead of leaping down in spectacular falls, descend in broken cascades ensconced in narrow slot-like gorges.

The prevailing depth of the Kings River's tributary valleys, again, is intimately linked with the extreme ruggedness of its flanking heights. These contrast with those of the Yosemite Valley as mountain peaks contrast with foothills. The Yosemite lies between unimpressive, billowy uplands, the individual swells on which are only 1000 to 1500 feet high—only one-third to one-half as high as the chasm itself is deep. The Yosemite is therefore easily the dominant feature of its district; there is little in its environment to distract the eye from it. The Kings River Canyon, on the other hand, is surrounded by a galaxy of peaks and crests many of which tower 4000 and even 5000 feet above its brinks—to twice the height of the chasm's own walls. To one who surveys the landscape from Lookout Point the disproportion is at once apparent, and yet, *mirabile dictu,* the chasm does not seem dwarfed, it loses not one jot in majesty, but rather gains by reason of its stupendous setting. And does not therein lie the real test of its inherent scenic grandeur? A chasm less sublime would sink into insignificance amid such titanic surroundings.

And now let us see how these various facts are to be explained. Through what circumstances is it that the Kings River Canyon and the Yosemite Valley have come to be so closely alike in some respects, though so unlike in others?

To begin with the most obvious: Both chasms unquestionably owe their broad trough form to repeated and intense glaciation. Their almost uniform U-shape and their sheer, spurless, parallel sides are characteristic features of glacier channels. But this does not necessarily imply that the chasms are products of glacier action alone or even mainly; it is clear from the positions of the moraines, as well as from many other things, that the chasms are stream-worn canyons that have been remodeled and enlarged by the ice, the transformation from the original V-shape to the final U-shape having been brought about by widening fully as much as by deepening.

Just what proportion of the total work of excavation in either chasm is to be attributed to glacier action and what proportion to preglacial stream action has long been a moot question, but today we are for the first time in a position to give the answer, for the Yosemite at least, in rather definite quantitative terms. For it has been found possible to determine the preglacial depth of that chasm within narrow limits, and consequently it is also possible now to compute the amount of rock that was excavated by stream and glacier respectively.

Indeed, the Yosemite is probably the first glaciated canyon whose preglacial dimensions and configuration have been ascertained in some detail.[2] Three favor-

---

[2] In sufficient detail to permit the drawing of a contour map from which a relief model of the preglacial Yosemite chasm can be constructed.

ing circumstances have rendered this possible: the presence of certain features in the Yosemite Valley that are fairly reliable indices of its preglacial depth; the availability of a topographic base of adequate accuracy for necessary measurements of height and distance (the map which the writer prepared in 1905–06); and the granting by the U. S. Geological Survey of sufficient time and funds for an intensive study of the problem.

As a result it can now be stated with some confidence that the Yosemite, prior to the advent of the glaciers, was fully 2400 feet deep, measured from the brow of El Capitan, and 2000 feet deep opposite Glacier Point. The additional deepening effected by the ice, therefore, ranges from 600 feet at the lower end to more than 1200 feet at the upper end of the chasm.[3]

For the Kings River Canyon no such definite figures can be given; indeed, it is doubtful whether any can ever be determined. But from the preliminary studies it seems reasonably certain that the depth of glacial cutting in the canyon was less, on the whole, than in the Yosemite, save at the extreme head, where it was about the same in both.

A word, next, about the broad, level floors that distinguish the Yosemite Valley and the Kings River Canyon from the typical U-troughs of the High Sierra. These floors are not products of glacial excavating, but due in each case to a filling of loose debris that conceals the bottom contours of the U-trough. In the Yosemite the rock floor was scooped out by the ice in the form of an elongated basin—the basin of ancient Lake Yosemite—and this basin was filled with sand and gravel deposited by the Merced River. In the Kings River Canyon probably no basin was excavated (there may possibly have been a shallow one near the upper end), but during the final recession of the glacier the floor was left deeply encumbered with ice-borne debris. The Kings River Glacier evidently was much more heavily loaded with rock-waste than the Yosemite Glacier, and not only left one moraine loop after another, but between moraines liberated immense quantities of gravel and boulders that were spread out in thick sheets by the torrents flowing from the melting ice. This outwash material now forms the greater part of the floor upon which one travels and camps; only the crests of the recessional moraines emerge here and there above it.

The difference in the nature of the filling in the two chasms accounts for the contrast in degree of flatness of their respective floors. The floor of the Yosemite is so nearly level that the eye can not detect its slope—it descends

[3] See footnote on page 62.—ED.

only twenty feet in a distance of five miles; whereas the floor of the Kings River Canyon descends 600 feet in a distance of nine miles, or at an average of sixty-six feet to the mile.

The great width of both chasms is due largely to the fact that the glaciers were able to "quarry" laterally to far better advantage in them than in the canyons above or below. This glacial quarrying was facilitated by the prevalence of "joints" in the rock—more or less regularly spaced fractures—whereby blocks of convenient size were made available for plucking and transportation. The canyons above and below, on the contrary, are narrow, because the rock in them was less generally fractured—in fact, for considerable distances it was wholly undivided—and as a consequence the glaciers could only grind and polish. And in the hard Sierra granites these abrasive processes work with exceeding slowness.

Another circumstance that doubtless contributed toward the production of the great width of the two chasms was the confluence at their heads of two powerful tributary glaciers. For it can be shown analytically that the consolidation of two or more glaciers into one is bound to result in a decided increase in economy of movement and a corresponding increase in kinetic energy (energy of mass movement due to gravitation) available for erosive action. But the importance of this factor should not be overrated, for there is ample evidence that a confluence of glaciers was not indispensable in every case in the Sierra Nevada for the production of a typical Yosemite. Instances are not wanting of such valleys whose heads are not marked by any junction of tributary glacier troughs. The Little Yosemite is a good example. In its case, certainly, the predominance of well-jointed and readily quarried rock is the prime factor that determined its great width.

Withal there are few places in the Sierra Nevada where the relative impotence of the ice when dealing with massive, undivided granite is more strikingly exemplified than in some parts of the Little Yosemite. Liberty Cap and Mount Broderick, the two great bosses that obstruct its mouth, stood directly in the path of the glacier, yet they have survived as gigantic *roches moutonnées,* each being essentially an unquarriable monolith.

There is, then, little doubt that both the Kings River Canyon and the Yosemite Valley have been developed in places where the joints in the rock permitted glacial quarrying on an extraordinary scale. Their broad trough form, accordingly, is a "function," as mathematicians would say, of their rock structure. Of course, it is a function also of the quarrying power of the glacier. That the Kings River Canyon is only one-half as wide and two-thirds as deep as the Yosemite is due in part to the inferior quarrying power of the Kings River Glacier and only in part to the less quarriable nature of its rocks. Space does not permit here for the giving of a comparison of the Kings River and Yosemite glaciers. Suffice it to say that their relative magnitudes and quarrying powers are readily inferred from their respective moraine systems, of which the writer was able to make a comparative study in the summer of 1925.

The detail sculpture of the cliffs of both chasms also is intimately associated with the varying structure of the rock. Indeed, each type of sculpture is the expression of a definite type of structure, and because of the delicacy of touch of the postglacial sculpturing agents—frost, temperature changes, running water, snow-slides, ground water, and so forth—every local change and vagary in the structure has been brought out in *bas-relief*.

The massive, undivided granite in general gives rise to rounded domes and curving walls—it tends to assume simple flowing outlines, because it "exfoliates" at the surface in smoothly curving concentric shells. The jointed rocks, on the other hand, are carved into prevailingly angular, faceted forms. And where these two types of structure intermingle in capricious fashion, there arise forms of unusual, striking individuality, monuments of unique design, such as Half Dome, Cathedral Rocks, the Grand Sentinel, and the Sphinx.

Two things account for the phenomenal array of bold and contrasting sculptural forms in the Yosemite Valley: the rather fortuitous assemblage within its compass of a number of differing types of rock, and the frequent occurrence of extreme types of structure in immediate juxtaposition. The upper Kings River Canyon owes its pronounced Yosemite-like sculpture likewise to the presence of granite of highly irregular structure; the lower part of the canyon, on the contrary, is cut in more evenly jointed rocks, and therefore is scenically less impressive.

What now may be the reason for the marked disparity between the two chasms in the matter of hanging valleys and waterfalls? In the last analysis it, too, is traceable to structural influences. The elevated hanging valleys of the Yosemite region are held up by massive granite exceedingly resistant to both stream and glacier erosion. One need but view the grand cliff under the upper Yosemite Falls to be convinced of this fact: most of its rock is wholly undivided to a height of a thousand feet, and what few master joints traverse the western portion are spaced hundreds of feet apart. On the other hand, the deeply cut side gorges of the Kings River Canyon, and the little gulches incised into the lips of its few hanging valleys, all traverse rocks sufficiently fractured to give the eroding agents a good hold.

But that, after all, is only a small part of the story. The significance of the hanging valleys themselves must be taken into account. They are the telltale features of the landscape that give us the key to the mysteries of the early history and the ultimate origin of the two chasms.

It has been commonly supposed that the hanging valleys whose waters pour into the Yosemite chasm are, like most hanging valleys in glaciated mountain regions, products of glaciation mainly; or, to state it more accurately, that they have remained suspended high above the chasm's floor largely because the feeble branch glaciers that occupied them were unable to excavate as effectively as the powerful Yosemite Glacier. Undeniably great disparity in eroding power between the main glacier and its tributaries was a potent factor in developing and accentuating the discordance between the main chasm and its side valleys, but one would greatly err in giving it sole credit for producing the entire discordance in every case.

As far back as 1913, when the farthest limits reached by the Yosemite Glacier were for the first time definitely mapped by the writer, it became evident that hanging valleys occur not only within the glaciated area of the Yosemite region, but also outside of it. A number of them actually occur on both sides of the lower Merced Canyon, many miles below El Portal, in whose vicinity the glacier terminated. A similar state of things has since been found in the unglaciated lower portions of Tuolumne, Stanislaus, and San Joaquin canyons. The ancient glaciers did not reach within thirty miles of the base of the range, yet typical hanging valleys, with cascades tumbling from their mouths, occur within a very few miles of the foothills.

How are these facts to be accounted for? Were the side streams, perhaps, unable to trench as rapidly as the master streams? And if so, why?

The Sierra Nevada, it is to be borne in mind, consists of a huge block of the earth's crust that lies strongly tilted, with its eastern edge raised to a great height above its western edge. Whenever the slope of a block range of this kind is sharply accentuated by renewed earth stresses, the streams that run down its back, finding their paths appreciably steepened, will flow with greatly increased velocity and correspondingly increased eroding power. As a consequence they will rapidly deepen their beds and in the course of time entrench themselves in narrow gorges. But with this rapid trenching their feebler tributaries will be unable to keep step, and this is true especially of those tributaries which flow at right angles to the direction of the tilting, for they remain unsteepened and unaccelerated. Inevitably, therefore, the valleys of these tributaries will be left suspended high above the main canyon—they will come to be "hanging" valleys, simply as a result of the uplift of the range and without the intervention of glacial processes.

Precisely this is what has happened in the Sierra Nevada. The Merced, flowing, as it does, directly down the western slope, as a result of the last strong tilting movement has been accelerated to torrential speed and ever since has been actively intrenching itself in a narrow gorge. But only its larger tributaries have been able to keep up with this trenching, the lesser ones, and especially those arranged at right angles to the direction of the tilting, having remained suspended high above the main canyon.

That this is the true explanation of the hanging side valleys of the unglaciated lower Merced Canyon there can be not the slightest doubt; but it is not so easy to decide in how far this explanation applies also to the hanging side valleys of

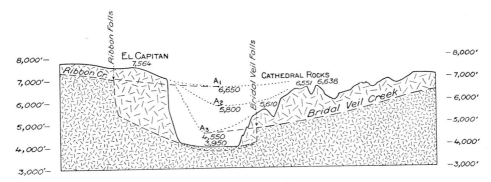

Figure 4.—Section across Yosemite Valley from El Capitan to the Cathedral Rocks. Projected on this section is another drawn along Ribbon Creek and Bridalveil Creek. The vertical and horizontal scales are strictly equal. By extending forward the profile of Ribbon Creek, whose hanging valleys belong to the upper set, there is found a former level (A_1) of the Merced River; A_2 is a lower level, indicated by the profiles of Indian Creek and the other hanging valleys of the middle set; and A_3 is a still lower level, indicated by the profile of lower Bridalveil Creek, whose gulch belongs to the lower set. There are thus indicated three successive stages in the cutting of the Yosemite chasm—what are believed to be the late Miocene, the late Pliocene, and the early Pleistocene. Glaciation did not set in until after the third stage (A_3) had been reached. The dotted lines show the approximate form of the chasm at each stage.

the profoundly glaciated Yosemite Valley. To settle that question the writer plotted accurately to scale the longitudinal profiles of all these hanging valleys, as well as of those along the lower Merced Canyon. Then, by extending the smooth curve of each profile forward over the axis of the main canyon (in the manner shown in Fig. 4), he determined the former level of the Merced to which each side valley had been adjusted. (Of course a correction had to be made in each case for the erosion effected in the side valley by stream or glacier since it was left hanging, but the corrections required were as a rule quite small and not difficult to evaluate.) All the A points, finally, were plotted on a longitudinal profile of the main canyon, and here is what was found:

There are in the Yosemite region three distinct sets of hanging valleys, disposed at different levels one above another. The valleys of Ribbon Creek, Yosemite Creek, and upper Bridalveil Creek belong to the upper set; the valleys of Illilouette Creek and Indian Creek belong to the middle set; the gulches of lower Bridalveil Creek and Cascade Creek belong to the lower set. The A points of each set, moreover, are remarkably accordant among themselves and establish unmistakably a former profile of the master stream. There are thus three such profiles, each indicating a definite stage in the cutting of the chasm.

Now the middle profile accords closely with the profile established by the hanging valleys in the lower Merced Canyon. It follows that the valleys of Illilouette Creek and Indian Creek owe their hanging character in the first instance to rapid gorge-cutting by the Merced in consequence of the last Sierra uplift. These valleys were hanging before glaciation set in, but their height has since been greatly increased by the glacial deepening and widening of the main chasm. It follows, further, that the upper set of hanging valleys is also of preglacial origin—that is, it became suspended as a result of rapid gorge-cutting induced by an earlier uplift. Only the lower set of valleys, or gulches, owes its height above the floor of the chasm to glaciation.

The story told by the hanging valleys of the Yosemite region, then, is a story of two long chapters of gorge-cutting by the Merced due to two great uplifts of the Sierra Nevada, followed by a chapter of glaciation.

The depth of the Yosemite at each stage being known, it is not difficult to draw its approximate cross-section for each stage (Fig. 4), and to determine its relations to the surrounding country. In this way it has been ascertained that the chasm began its existence as a broad, flat valley only a few hundred feet deep, flanked by a lowland covered with rolling hills. The present billows on the uplands are these same hills lifted to a higher level. In the second stage the Yosemite had the depth and aspect of a mountain valley. It was cut about 1000 feet below the rolling country on either side and already had hanging side valleys from whose mouths the waters descended in broken cascades. In the third stage the Yosemite had the appearance of a rugged canyon with a narrow inner gorge, its total depth averaging about 2500 feet. It had two sets of hanging valleys, a high and a low one, and its sides consequently were adorned by many glorious cascades. Finally the canyon was profoundly remodeled—deepened and widened —by the glaciers of the Ice Age, and its cascades were transformed to leaping waterfalls.

There being no fossil-bearing deposits in the Yosemite region, the writer at first was at a loss to find a way to determine the geologic age of any of its pre-glacial stages. In 1921, however, he succeeded in carrying his work northward to the nearest locality where fossils are known to occur. This locality was none other than Table Mountain—the Table Mountain where resided Bret Harte's Truthful James! And there the writer was fortunate enough to be guided to the right spot by that veteran miner and lover of the earth sciences, Mr. J. B. Pownall, of Stockton and Sonora, and excellent casts of leaves from the hardened silts of a "fossil stream channel" were secured. Through the courtesy of Dr. John C. Merriam, again, the casts were submitted for identification to Dr. Ralph W. Chaney, Research Associate of the Carnegie Institution; and by him they were pronounced to be in all probability of late Miocene age.[4] And thus it has been established, as definitely as is possible with the scanty palaeontologic material at hand, that the earliest recognizable stage of the Yosemite Valley—that indicated by the upper set of hanging valleys—antedated the close of the Miocene epoch. The first great uplift, it may be presumed, therefore, took place about the dawn of the Pliocene epoch, and it was during that epoch that the first set of hanging valleys was produced. The second uplift took place probably about the close of the Pliocene, and consequently, by the beginning of the Pleistocene epoch (which included the Ice Age), the second set of valleys was suspended.

In the present landscape of the Yosemite region, then, the billowy uplands and their associated hanging valleys represent remnants of the ancient landscape of late Miocene time, preserved by reason of the exceedingly resistant

[4] See Appendix for table showing Major Divisions of Geologic Time in use by the U. S. Geological Survey, and the time values for these divisions as determined by the Committee on the Measurement of Geologic Time, National Research Council.—ED.

nature of the massive granite. The valleys of Illilouette Creek and Indian Creek, which lie at a considerably lower level, are remnants of the Pliocene landscape, somewhat modified by glaciation; and the gulch of Bridalveil Creek is a prominent feature of the early Pleistocene canyon stage of the Yosemite that has escaped destruction by the ice.

In the Kings River region, owing to the poor preservation of the hanging valleys, and also because of the lack of an accurate large-scale map, the successive stages in the development of the main chasm are much more difficult to determine. Nor is it easy to single out remnants of the Miocene and Pliocene landscapes on the flanking mountain massifs. Indeed, but for the guidance afforded by the analyses made in the Yosemite region and in other parts of the Sierra Nevada, probably little headway would be possible in the spelling out of the story of the development of the Kings River Canyon. As it is, however, much can be accomplished in spite of the existing handicaps.

There is little doubt, for instance, that Mount Mitchell, the level upland to the north of it, and all of Sentinel Ridge are remnants, almost untouched by the ice of glacial times, of the late Miocene landscape. Other remnants of this

Figure 5.—Section across Kings River Canyon from Goat Crest, on the Monarch Divide, over North Dome and the Grand Sentinel to Palmer Mountain. Projected on this section is another drawn along Granite Creek and Roaring River. The vertical and horizontal scales are equal. A_1 represents what is believed to be the late Miocene stage in the development of the chasm, indicated by the extended profile of Granite Basin; A_2 represents the late Pliocene stage, indicated by the extended profile of Cloud Canyon; and A_3 represents the early Pleistocene (preglacial) stage, indicated by the lower valley of Granite Creek. (All such determinations are necessarily tentative.)

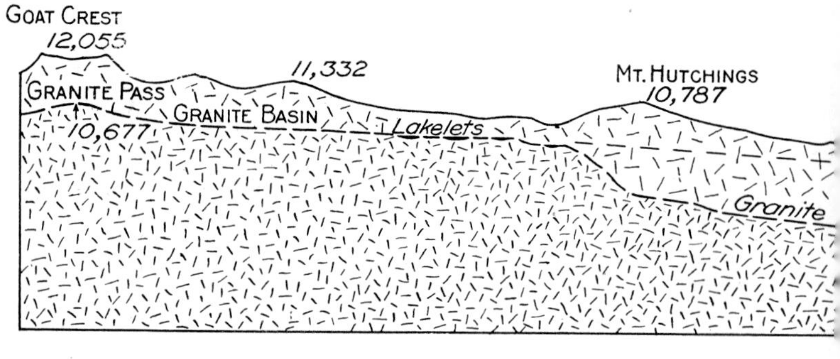

landscape, more or less glaciated, may be identified on the crest of the Monarch Divide. Of these, Granite Basin, indeed all of the elevated upper valley of Granite Creek, is of peculiar interest; for its longitudinal profile, extended forward to the axis of the main chasm (Fig. 5), would seem to indicate the approximate level of the master stream for that early epoch. The South Fork, it will be seen, then lay in a wide-flaring valley 3600 feet shallower than the present chasm, yet already carved 3000 feet below the summits of the Monarch Divide.

Again, there is reason to believe that the longitudinal profile of Cloud Canyon (not shown in Fig. 5), duly corrected for glaciation, indicates the level to which the main chasm was cut during Pliocene time. Sugarloaf Valley probably also belongs to the ancient landscape of that epoch. Finally, it is not impossible that the lower valley of Granite Creek affords some indication of the depth of cutting achieved by the South Fork immediately prior to the coming of the glaciers.

Thus, tentatively and by degrees, one may find the way into an analysis of the features of the Kings River region. Possibly someday when that region shall be included in a great national park, as it well deserves to be, a more detailed map of it will become available, and the foundation will be laid for an intensive and quantitative study such as has been made of the Yosemite Valley. What a wonderful thesis for a future student of geomorphology that would be!

Reprinted from Sierra Club Bulletin, *1926, pages 224–236.*

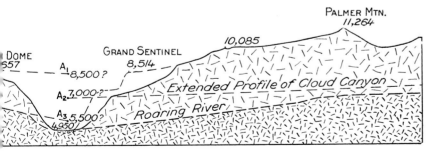

THE DEVIL'S POSTPILE

AND ITS

STRANGE SETTING

THE SIERRA NEVADA, geologists tell us, consists essentially of one vast block of the earth's crust that lies tilted toward the southwest, its northeastern edge elevated to form the crest line. The surface of the block, in general, slopes gently down to the Great Valley of California; the steep eastern side, exposed by the uplift, and in part, probably, by the subsidence of the earth blocks underlying Owens Valley and the Mono Basin, forms the imposing eastward-facing mountain front. A cross-section of the Sierra Nevada, accordingly, is like that shown, with vertical dimension somewhat exaggerated in Figure 6.

To an aviator soaring high above the range, its block form and its westerly slant are readily manifest, but to the mountaineer who, like a pygmy ant, crawls among the peaks and canyons of its surface, they are not obvious. Only from some of the higher summits on the main crest can he obtain a sufficiently comprehensive view to perceive the general form of the range. A great satisfaction it is, if you have the tilted-block concept in mind, to see it thus impressively demonstrated: Southwestward from Mount Dana or Mount Whitney, for instance, the range falls away gradually, its slope diversified by minor crests and ridges; to the northeast it drops off with amazing abruptness, to a depth of more than 6000 feet from the summit of Mount Dana, to a depth of 11,000 feet from Mount Whitney. To the northwest and the southeast the crest of the range extends as far as the eye can see, studded with boldly sculptured peaks. There is additional satisfaction in finding that, although the range is deeply furrowed by canyons and gulches, the divide between the easterly and westerly waters coincides in the main with the crest line.

Devil's Postpile, Devil's Postpile
National Monument, California. By William Hail

If now you are fully convinced of the soundness of the tilted-block idea, and if perchance you are inclined to feel cocksure about it—even scientists occasionally have spells of cocksureness, 'tis only human—take yourself to the headwaters of the Middle Fork of the San Joaquin, the land of the Devil's Postpile, the Mammoth Pass, and the Ritter Range. There the main crest of the Sierra Nevada sags down ignominiously to a low, flattish ridge, a third-rate feature of the sort that elsewhere in the Sierra Nevada would scarcely attract attention. No alpine "High Sierra" here, nor any amazing drop to the eastern foot of the range! From the Mammoth Pass the descent to the east is only 1500 feet, and from the saddle north of Mammoth Mountain, which is slightly lower than the pass, the descent is even less, and mostly in the form of a slope.

Figure 6

It is rather disturbing to one's ideas of the nature of a tilted-block range, further, to discover that the canyon of the Middle Fork, immediately west of the saddle in the divide, is considerably lower than the country to the east. The altitude of Pumice Flat, north of the Devil's Postpile, is 7700 to 7800 feet; that of Reds Meadow 7500 feet; the saddle in the divide is about 9300 feet, and the sloping plain directly east of the saddle averages over 8000 feet. To enhance the anomaly of the situation, there rises, west of the Middle Fork, an exceptionally bold, spectacular group of mountains that dwarfs the divide into insignificance —the group of which Banner Peak, Mount Ritter, and the Minarets are the principal summits. Over 13,000 feet in altitude, Mount Ritter towers more than a mile above Pumice Flat and the Devil's Postpile, and fully 3800 feet above the saddle in the divide. Even Mammoth Mountain is outtopped more than 2000 feet. A profile line over the Ritter Range, across Pumice Flat, and over the divide, plotted without vertical exaggeration from the contour lines of the topographic map, turns out as shown in Figure 7.

How are these singular facts to be reconciled with the tilted-block form of the Sierra Nevada? Or is that form only a myth? Why is the main divide near the Devil's Postpile so much lower than the Ritter Range? Why is not that lofty range, which connects at the north with Mount Lyell, itself the divide? How did the Middle Fork of the San Joaquin, which heads on the east flank of Banner Peak, succeed in cutting its canyon around the southern end of the Ritter Range? Why is the floor of its canyon in the vicinity of the Devil's Postpile so much lower than the country east of the divide? And what, finally, is the real nature of the Devil's Postpile? These are the questions that anyone who has visited the region is bound to ask himself.

It will be a comfort to those who still have a lingering faith in the tilted-block theory to note, in the first place, that though the crest of the Sierra Nevada in the vicinity of the Devil's Postpile seems strangely low, nevertheless its lowest

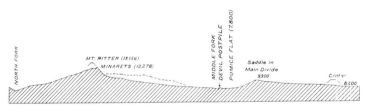

Figure 7

saddle, north of Mammoth Mountain, is only 600 feet lower than the Tioga Pass, which thrills the motorist with its great altitude (9941 feet). The fact is, the main divide near Mammoth Mountain is not abnormally low for the central part of the Sierra Nevada. It merely seems low because it is overshadowed by the Ritter Range and because the drop to the country to the east is slight. The latter circumstance is, however, readily explained by the fact that the country east of the divide is built up with volcanic materials—lava and pumice. The total thickness of these materials can only be surmised, but it is probably not less than 2000 feet. The pumice alone must have great thickness, for it forms the long slope, more than 1000 feet high, that leads up to within 300 feet of the saddle in the divide. There can be no doubt that it conceals bold cliffs, and it may reasonably be supposed that if the pumice and the other volcanic materials underneath were removed, there would be found here, as elsewhere along the northeast flank of the Sierra Nevada, an abrupt and imposing escarpment.

What is this pumice, and whence did it come? It consists of small fragments and lumps of highly siliceous lava, literally steam-shredded, that were blown by spasmodic explosions from a series of craters to the east of the range. There are fully thirty of these craters, extending in a row from Mammoth Mountain northward to Mono Lake. Some are only a few hundred feet high, the largest more than 2000 feet. Their alignment (see Mount Lyell quadrangle) suggests strongly that they are associated with a great fracture, or a zone of fractures, in the crust of the earth. The bulk of the pumice naturally showered down immediately about the craters from which it was ejected, but the finer particles drifted some distance with the wind, and as a consequence there is a sprinkling of pumice over a considerable part of the Sierra Nevada. The Mammoth Pass and the divide for several miles to the north are most thickly covered, and Pumice Flat, as its name implies, is well supplied with it. Even at Reds Meadows and farther south along the Middle Fork there is a thin veneer of pumice. The dust it creates wears the skin off one's fingers, as those who have camped in those parts have reason to remember.

The fractures in the earth, indicated by the row of craters mentioned, in all probability do not stop at the foot of the Sierra Nevada, but penetrate some distance into the body of the range. For not only does Mammoth Mountain, itself the remnant of an old volcano, stand in line with them, but so do the little Red Cones perched on the east side of the canyon of the Middle Fork, and Pumice Butte, north of Fish Creek. The famous hot spring near Reds Meadow, though somewhat west of the line, doubtless is connected with it.

A bubbling hot spring of this type, it is now realized, is essentially a volcanic phenomenon. It is fed in part by steam emanating from hot lava in process of crystallization, in part by surface water that has seeped down to great depths and has been heated by the steam. Water generated directly by igneous rocks is what geologists please to call "juvenile" water, in distinction to "meteoric" water, which falls upon the earth from the clouds. Let those who would make their ablutions in the hot spring bear this in mind. Perhaps they will feel rejuvenated as well as cleansed, if only as a result of the therapeutic value of the thought that the water is in part new-born, straight from Mother Earth.

Volcanism appears to have been active along the line of fractures at widely different dates in geologic history. The explosions of pumice represent but the latest chapter. They began toward the end of the Ice Age, and continued at intervals probably until fairly recent times. It is certain in any event that the pumice at Reds Meadow fell a long time after the Middle Fork Glacier had melted back to its source. Mammoth Mountain, on the other hand, dates back to preglacial time, and must be well over a million years old. By the long-continued disintegration of its volcanic rock it has long since lost its original crater form and has been reduced to a shapeless hump.

Intermediate between the formation of Mammoth Mountain and the eruptions from the pumice craters there occurred another remarkable volcanic outbreak: Right in the Mammoth Pass a fissure opened and let forth a flood of black basaltic lava. By far the greater part of this fluid material poured into the canyon of the Middle Fork and there spread out in an elongated mass that

Devil's Postpile, Devil's Postpile National Monument, California. By Cedric Wright

extended from the head of Pumice Flat southward beyond the site of the Rainbow Falls. The total length of this mass (which may possibly have been supplied in part from other vents) was about six miles; its thickness ranged from 100 to perhaps 700 feet. The outpouring took place during the interglacial epoch that preceded the last glaciation in the Sierra Nevada—presumably between 100,000 and 200,000 years ago.

The Middle Fork Glacier, when for the last time it readvanced, found this mass of basalt obstructing its path. Being about 1000 feet thick, it had no difficulty in overriding the obstruction. Moreover, the basalt, having cracked into columns by contraction while cooling, was readily quarried away by the glacier, column by column. During the thousands of years that the ice held sway, therefore, most of the basalt was removed and the canyon re-excavated nearly, in places all the way down to the granite. Only the more obdurate parts of the basalt mass were left standing. Of these the largest is that strange hump in the middle of the canyon, about 300 yards long and 200 feet high, which, because of the fancied resemblance of its tall, straight columns to posts stacked together in upright position, has been facetiously—and quite aptly—named the Devil's Postpile.

A mere hummock in a landscape dominated by mile-high peaks, the Devil's Postpile is nevertheless a feature of unusual interest to the scientist as well as to the layman. The columns that form its steep west front, facing the river, are exceptionally high, straight and cleancut; those at its southern end are remarkable for their curvature and their radial arrangement with respect to a center at the top of the pile. Strikingly beautiful, also, are the six-sided or five-sided end facets of the columns which in places still gleam with the polish that was imparted to them by the overriding glacier.

But now let us return to the interpretation of the larger features of the region. The full significance of the broad sag in the crest of the range is yet to be revealed. In all likelihood it is the mouth of an ancient valley which extended far to the eastward and whose stream emptied into the Middle Fork of the San Joaquin at that remote epoch when the Sierra block was not yet uptilted and when the waters from the country to the east still drained seaward across its surface. At that time, of course, the Middle Fork had not yet cut its profound canyon, but flowed in a relatively shallow valley slightly below the level of the sag and below the shoulders that now flank the canyon. It seems probable, furthermore, in view of the depth and breadth of the sag (Mammoth Mountain did not then exist), that the valley indicated by it was the pathway of a large river—indeed, of the main San Joaquin—and that that part of the present Middle Fork which pursues a southeasterly course from Thousand Island Lake to the Devil's Postpile was merely a tributary of the master stream. The San Joaquin River, as we now know it, therefore appears to be a "beheaded" stream, its original upper course having been cut off by the uptilting of the Sierra block. Several other Sierra streams beside the San Joaquin, that now begin in gaps in the crest of the range, doubtless were similarly decapitated.

It is significant that, although the main San Joaquin flows southwestward, quite normally down the slope of the range, a number of its tributaries have southeasterly or northwesterly courses, in disregard of the general slant of the Sierra block. Not only the head of the Middle Fork, but the North Fork, Granite Creek, and Chiquito Creek have southeasterly courses; Fish Creek and the South Fork have northwesterly courses. All owe their trends to the constraining influence of more or less prominent ridges that themselves have a general northwest-southeast trend. A similar state of things is found in certain parts of the drainage basins of the Merced, Tuolumne, Kings, and Kaweah rivers. There is a definite reason for this. The area now occupied by the Sierra Nevada bore at an earlier time in geologic history—namely, during the Cretaceous period[1]—

Figure 8

a series of roughly parallel mountain ranges that had a general northwest-southeast trend. Although this ancient mountain system, as a result of stream erosion during more than a hundred million years, was in large part worn down before the Sierra block first became outlined and gained a westerly slant, nevertheless a number of the higher northwest-southeast ranges and the valley troughs between them were perpetuated. The new Sierra Nevada, therefore, inherited these features from the ancestral mountain system. When the Sierra block was uptilted, all the ranges and valleys on its surface were tilted with it. Indeed, our Sierra Nevada is to be regarded as something greater than a simple mountain range. It is of the order of a mountain system. Its areal extent equals that of all the Swiss, French, and most of the Italian Alps together!

The ancient mountain ranges of the Cretaceous period were not block ranges. They were carved from great wrinkles in the crust of the earth (Fig. 8) produced by the compression and folding of a series of strata that lay originally flat, having been deposited on the floor of the ocean—strata of sandstone, limestone, shale, and clay aggregating at least a mile in thickness. While the folding was in progress molten granite surged up and invaded the folds from below. Squeezed by the intense pressure and baked by the heat of the granite, the

[1] See footnote on page 97, and Appendix.—ED.

stratified rocks were "metamorphosed" to quartzite, marble, schist, and slate. Large bodies of these metamorphic rocks still remain in different parts of the Sierra Nevada, and by their contorted structure give evidence of the former existence of the mountain ranges, and even indicate their trend, their parallelism, and their general character, which must have been analogous to that of the present Appalachian Mountains. As a matter of fact the geologist finds incorporated in the Sierra block remnants of two such series of folded strata that differ widely in age, and thus he knows that two systems of mountains have in turn occupied the place of the present Sierra Nevada in times gone by.

The foothills and the choppy ridges through which the Merced River cuts its canyon below the Yosemite are composed largely of these metamorphic rocks. The mountains fronting upon the Mono Basin similarly are made of them. Some of the high crests that have inherited their northwesterly trends from the mountains of the Cretaceous period consist of smaller bodies. The Le Conte Divide, near the head of the South Fork of the San Joaquin, is a notable example. The Ritter Range is another but rather complicated example. The structure of the metamorphic rocks is most readily traced along its northeast base. The beds there stand vertical or at high angles, and have northwesterly trends. Gray schists and variously colored quartzites predominate. The upper canyon of the Middle Fork, from Pumice Flat to Thousand Island Lake, cuts lengthwise through these rocks and to them probably owes its position and its trend. The Ritter Range itself is composed in part of dark mottled rocks that represent ancient lavas metamorphosed out of all semblance to their former selves. Associated with these is a complex of dark igneous rocks that doubtless were injected in a molten state into the arch of one of the great upfolds of the ancient mountains. It is the exceedingly obdurate nature of these rocks that has permitted the Ritter Range to maintain its great height. The range notably terminates at the south where these rocks end. When, therefore, you climb Mount Ritter, you climb the core of one of the ancestral mountains that were formed more than a hundred million years before the present Sierra Nevada was uplifted.

Reprinted from Sierra Club Bulletin, *1930, pages 1–8.*

THE LITTLE

"LOST VALLEY"

ON SHEPHERD'S CREST

LAST SUMMER, while roaming over the High Sierra with the Scout Naturalist Expedition, it was my good fortune to become acquainted with a piece of mountain sculpture of a very exceptional sort.[1] Though presumably not without parallel in the Sierra Nevada, it is nevertheless of a type that from the very nature of things cannot be represented by more than a few examples. The feature in question is on the top of the mountain known as Shepherd's Crest, which stands forth prominently on the east side of Virginia Canyon, a mile or more above the McCabe Lakes. To many members of the Sierra Club, doubtless, this mountain is a familiar landmark; for all I know, it has been climbed and explored from end to end; but to me it was new and its summit sculpture a revelation, the more unexpected since the small-scale topographic map, which I had duly scanned in advance, gave scarcely a hint of its unusualness.

Viewed from any low point to the southwest, Shepherd's Crest appears surmounted by a row of blunt pinnacles, all curved in the same direction, and rising from a sheer wall that is cleft at almost regular intervals. Not having seen the mountain before, one might readily suppose these jagged teeth to constitute the main summit crest; but on viewing it from other directions and from higher vantage-points, one perceives that there is a second crest, higher and smoother, some distance to the north of the first. Between them lies a bit of rolling upland that seems wholly unrelated to the sheer glacier-trimmed sides of the mountain, and, what is most remarkable, this bit of upland consists of a

[1] The topographic features referred to in this essay are in the headwaters area of the Tuolumne River. See the topographic map of Yosemite National Park.—ED.

V-shaped valley instead of a convexly moulded summit. From each of the two confining crests the surface slopes inward to an old stream-channel that drains out at the western point of the mountain. This channel is, however, much nearer to the low southern crest than to the high northern crest, which culminates in a summit almost 400 feet above the valley, and so the feature as a whole is strikingly asymmetric.

The accompanying photographs, taken by members of the Scout Naturalist

Shepherd's Crest from the southwest. By Robert Branstead

Expedition, will help to make clear the odd configuration of the little valley. There are added a sketch map and a bird's-eye view designed to bring out its character more completely; these are based merely on the topographic map, the photographs, and my own observations, not on instrumental surveys of any sort. The little upland area, it will be seen, is roughly triangular in outline, and measures three-quarters of a mile in length from northwest to southeast, and one-quarter of a mile in greatest breadth. Its lowest point, at the lip of the valley, is just above the 11,500-foot contour line; the highest point on the northern crest reaches an altitude of 11,860 feet. The floor of Virginia Canyon, near by, is somewhat below 9000 feet.

In the view from Mount Conness (below), Shepherd's Crest is discernible in the left middle distance, mainly by the gentle slope that leads up to its high northern crest. The little valley itself is not visible; being masked by the pinnacled southern crest, nor is its actual extent apparent, yet its isolated position amidst the titanic environment of craggy peaks and profound canyons is almost dramatically revealed. It seems like a little secluded skyland realm, cut off from the fierce world around it by impregnable cliffs.

Looking north from Mount Conness. In the lower part of the view is the nivated west slope of North Peak. A bit of the upland surface on Shepherd's Crest is visible in the left middle distance, at the far end of a long arête. By Richard M. Leonard

That this little "lost valley," as the boys called it, is a lone remnant, a surviving bit of an ancient landscape of moderate relief that once had wide extent, but that has been largely consumed by the incision and widening of the deep newer canyons, readily suggests itself to one who observes it critically. Certainly to a geologist trained in the interpretation of topographic forms the fact is at once manifest from the very contrast between the flowing contours of the little upland valley and the stark sculpture of the canyon walls below. Moreover, in the foreground of the view from Mount Conness one beholds the smooth westerly slope of North Peak, which is in the same general range of altitudes as the valley on Shepherd's Crest and represents another remnant of the same ancient landscape. On the west it connects with still other smoothly curving remnants on Sheep Peak (not visible in photo on page 111). To the southeast of Mount Conness, again, one looks down upon a gently sloping tableland that exhibits the same subdued style of topography at the same general level. Farther to the southeast is the long flattish top of White Mountain, and beyond that the nearly level Dana Plateau, the largest tabular summit of this type. To the east

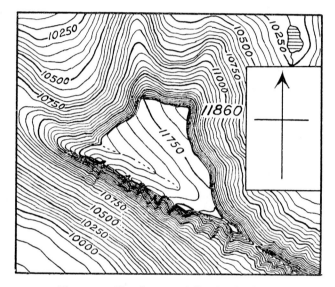

Figure 9.—Sketch map of Shepherd's Crest

and the northeast of Mount Conness, finally, are the smoothly rounded summits of the Tioga Crest, about three miles in aggregate length.

Though these different fragments of the ancient landscape (or erosion surface, as geomorphologists would term it) lie so far apart that the missing portions between them can hardly be reconstructed in imagination, it is possible, nevertheless, to make local restorations and to visualize to some extent the progressive destruction of the old topography by the development of the new. There can be no reasonable doubt, for instance, that the long attentuated arête which ties Shepherd's Crest to the main divide of the Sierra Nevada was once a massive ridge broad enough to bear a strip of the ancient topography throughout its entire length. By the glacial enlargement of the deep canyons on both sides to capacious cirques it has been gradually reduced in width until now there is left only a thin, sharp knife-ridge, a cleaver,[2] as such a feature would be termed in the Mount Rainier country. By the divergence of the two cirque glaciers Shepherd's Crest and its little upland valley happily were saved from a similar fate, but the broadening of the cirques nevertheless has progressed far enough to destroy in large part the two spurs of the upland topography that originally flanked the little valley. The two crests that now enclose it are not the tops of those ancient spurs—they are merely the sharp edges in which the encroaching cirque walls without cut the gentle slopes of the valley within.

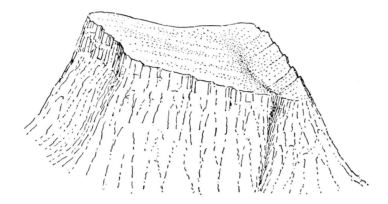

Figure 10.—Bird's-eye view of the Little Lost Valley
on Shepherd's Crest

But has not the little valley itself been glaciated? you will ask. No, it exhibits none of the characteristic signs of glaciation—that is, of erosion by a moving ice mass shod with rocks. According to the report of Scoutmaster Richard M. Leonard, who with several of the boys climbed up to the little valley by way of the spur that leads to its lip, polished and striated, or even simply smoothed rock-surfaces and rounded ledges, such as are common features of glacier-beds, are wholly absent from it; neither are there any accumulations of rock debris resembling moraines. On the other hand, he found its slopes encumbered throughout with angular blocks, large and small, loosened and heaved by the freezing of water in joints and crevices; and most of these blocks, he observed,

---

[2] Might not the expressive English word *cleaver* be more generally adopted in our vocabulary of mountain terms, in place of the alien and often mispronounced *arête,* thus leading the way, perhaps, to the expulsion of terrible *bergschrunds* and fanciful *roches moutonnées?*—F. E. M.

lie on or near their places of origin—no forces other than those of frost, snow-pressure, and gravity, apparently, have acted upon them. Such a mantle of frost-riven fragments is a characteristic feature of high mountain slopes that have borne no active glaciers, but only inert drifts or fields of snow. It is the product of that slow and unspectacular rock-shattering process due to oft-repeated alternations of frost and thaw, unaccompanied by any adequate transporting agency, for which some years ago I proposed the term *nivation,* in contradistinction to *glaciation.*[3]

While alternating freezings and thawings occur almost everywhere at high altitudes, the special combination of conditions that results in nivation occurs typically only on high summits and slopes that annually bear snowdrifts for long periods. For both the recurring drifts and the porous rock mantle tend to prevent the melt-water from gathering into vigorous transporting and eroding streams, and instead to distribute it into many feeble rills. Nivated slopes, accordingly, not only are mantled with rock debris that remains *in situ* (except as it is affected by local creeping movements known as "soil flow"),[4] but they are devoid of sharply cut stream-channels as well.

The little valley on Shepherd's Crest exhibits both of these effects of nivation. Its sides are rock-strewn throughout, and also unfurrowed by stream-worn ravines. Nevertheless, these facts alone cannot be accepted as absolute proof of its non-glaciation, for it is conceivable that the little valley was glaciated at a very early date in the Ice Age—so long ago that the nivation process has since had time to obliterate all traces of ice wear. At least three, and possibly four epochs[5] of glaciation have been recognized in the Sierra Nevada, and the earliest of these occurred presumably not less than half a million years ago. Such a span of time might have been long enough to give the little valley a thoroughly nivated aspect. However, it is to be observed that the valley retains the V-shape characteristic of stream erosion as well as remnants of a stream-channel, now appar-

---

[3] Matthes, F. E. Glacial sculpture in the Bighorn Mountains, Wyoming: *U. S. Geological Survey, 21st Annual Report, part 2,* 1900, pp. 167–190.

[4] Soil flow is relatively rare on the granitic peaks of the Sierra Nevada, but evidences of it were observed last summer on the Dana Plateau. Both nivation and soil flow are common phenomena in Alaska, and they occur on a large scale in northern Greenland, where, in spite of the high latitude, no glaciers ever existed.

[5] Blackwelder, Eliot. Pleistocene glaciation in the Sierra Nevada and Basin Ranges: *Geological Society of America Bull.,* vol. 42, 1931, pp. 865–922.

Matthes, F. E. Geologic history of the Yosemite Valley: *U. S. Geol. Survey Prof. Paper 160,* 1930.

ently no longer functional, at the bottom of the V. These facts constitute almost irrefutable proof of non-glaciation, for even moderate glacial action would have sufficed, considering the jointed structure of the granite of Shepherd's Crest, to remodel the valley into a fairly smooth U-shape and to wipe the central stream-channel out of existence; and no amount of nivation would have transformed a glacial U-shape back to a V-shape, or would have produced a new central channel. Its distinct V-shape, therefore, together with its nivated aspect, proves conclusively that the little valley on Shepherd's Crest has remained unglaciated.

Perhaps it will seem as though this conclusion had been reached with needless caution; but it is to be borne in mind that a hollow feature such as a valley is inherently well-adapted for the catchment of large quantities of snow and for the generation of a glacier—much better adapted than a tabular or convex

Ancient landscape on North Peak, Mount Conness in right background. Taken from the top of the avalanche chute at the head of Little Lost Valley. The nivated slope of North Peak contrasts strikingly with the glacial sculpture roundabout. By Alfred Dole

summit. The non-glaciation of the little valley on Shepherd's Crest therefore seemed rather unexpected, and it called for particularly convincing proof.

Such proof having been found, there opens at once a new vista of thought on the subject of the non-glaciation of the high tabular summits of the Sierra Nevada in general. All the tabular summits I have been able to examine bear the earmarks of prolonged nivation, yet corroborative evidence of their non-glaciation is not in every instance afforded by their topography. However, if the valley on Shepherd's Crest has definitely escaped glaciation, then the presumption is all the stronger that these tabular summits—or at least a large proportion of them—have escaped glaciation also.

Now, these summits, mark you, are situated in the highest parts of the range, whence emanated the mighty ice-streams of the glacial epoch—ice-streams that attained lengths of thirty to sixty miles and depths of 2000 to 4000 feet. Shepherd's Crest itself stands between two large cirques that formerly held glaciers a thousand to fifteen hundred feet in thickness, and it fronts on Virginia Canyon, which was the pathway of a trunk glacier fourteen miles in length and 2000 feet in thickness. The unglaciated slope on North Peak and the gently sloping platform to the southeast of Mount Conness are both literally surrounded by deep cirques that sent forth good-sized ice-streams. The same is true of the level top of White Mountain, of the Dana Plateau, of the tabular summits of Mount Gibbs, Kuna, Koip, and Blacktop peaks, and amongst many others farther south, of Mount Darwin and Mount Whitney. How then, it may be asked, does it happen that all these high-level tracts have escaped the heavy hand of the ice which wrought destruction all around them?

One reason readily suggests itself from the fact that they are all so oriented as to be exposed to the heat of the midday sun as well as to the southwesterly winds—which are the prevailing winds in the High Sierra, as is so eloquently attested by the asymmetric and even recumbent forms of the timberline trees. Everyone of the tabular summits and slopes before mentioned is inclined to the southwest, the west, or the south. Even the little valley on Shepherd's Crest, although its axis trends northwestward, has in the main southwesterly exposure, for the row of pinnacles on its southern edge is too low to create a "wind shadow" of any consequence. Moreover, any westerly air-currents that enter the little valley at its lip must in part be deflected by the high northern crest so as to turn directly up the valley.

Now, it is a fact of observation that the southwesterly winds blow the bulk of the snow, while it is still in a powdery state, from the exposed slopes up over the mountain crests, and fling it in great banners, as Muir aptly called them, out to the northeast, to let it swirl down at last in the sheltered valley below. Whatever snowdrifts remain untouched by the wind are later consumed by the rays of the sun, and so toward midsummer all southwesterly and southerly mountain sides are wholly bared, whereas the northeasterly and northerly sides are still generously flecked with snow, and in some places even retain perennial ice bodies.

In an article which he published in the *Sierra Club Bulletin,* as well as in the *Journal of Geology,* the late Dr. G. K. Gilbert[6] pointed out that during the Ice Age this markedly unequal distribution of snow, due to the combined action of wind and sun, must have tended to minimize glacial action on the southwesterly and southerly sides of the mountain crests and to intensify it on their northeasterly and northerly sides. As a consequence, many of these crests are now decidedly asymmetric in form, their southwesterly and southerly sides sloping at moderate angles, and their northeasterly and northerly sides being very abrupt, in part composed of unscalable cliffs. Dr. Gilbert saw, furthermore, that this asymmetry becomes more pronounced toward the lower levels of the High Sierra, where the windswept and sunny slopes were only feebly glaciated, and that it reaches an optimum at what may be termed the lower limit of glacier generation, where small glaciers could exist only on the sheltered northerly and northeasterly sides of the ridges, and where the southerly and southwesterly slopes remained wholly unglaciated. The contrast there is between the hacked-in headwalls of small cirques, on the one hand, and the gentle contours due to normal weathering and stream erosion, on the other hand. But, curiously, Dr. Gilbert did not complete his analysis. He did not see that the asymmetry of the crests becomes more pronounced also toward the upper levels of the High Sierra, and reaches another optimum on the lofty, tabular summit peaks, where the contrast again is between intense glaciation, on the one hand, and complete non-glaciation, on the other.

Three circumstances account for the non-glaciation of the tabular summit peaks of the Sierra Nevada and the little valley on Shepherd's Crest: First, the southwesterly winds attain much greater velocity and sweeping power at the crest of the range than at lower levels on its west slope; second, because of the

---

[6] Gilbert, G. K. Systematic asymmetry of crest lines in the High Sierra of California: *Journal of Geology,* vol. xii, no. 7, 1904, pp. 579–588; *Sierra Club Bulletin,* vol. v, 1905, pp. 279–286.

cold and the dryness of the air at the higher altitudes, the snow there remains longer in a powdery state and susceptible of being shifted about by the wind; and third, less snow falls in the winter on the main summit peaks than at levels 2000 to 3000 feet lower down. The last statement, it is true, is not supported by actual measurements of snow at different elevations on the west slope, but it may

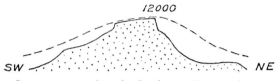

On extreme summit peaks. Southwest side nivated only.
Example, Dana Plateau

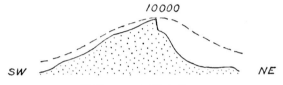

Halfway up in High Sierra.
Both sides glaciated, but southwest side only moderately.
Example, Mount Hoffmann

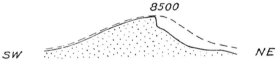

At lower level of glacier generation. Southwest side unglaciated.
Example, Horse Ridge, near Ostrander Lake

Figure 11.—Profiles of asymmetric crests in
Sierra Nevada.

safely be inferred from the fact that the clouds which blow in from the Pacific Ocean discharge the bulk of their snow approximately at the level at which they strike the chilling body of the range—at altitudes between 8000 and 11,000 feet.[7] Thence upward they inevitably discharge diminishing quantities as they rise toward the summit. In these respects the conditions in the Sierra Nevada are analogous to those that obtain in many other mountain ranges of great height, notably the Swiss Alps, the Pyrenees, the Caucasus, and the Andes of South

[7] These figures are for the latitude of the Yosemite region. They are rough approximations. More accurate data are desired.

America. In all these ranges the zone of maximum snow precipitation is known to lie several thousand feet below the summit peaks.

During the more severe climate of the glacial epoch, naturally, the snow-clouds hung even lower on the Sierra Nevada than they do today, and the zone of maximum snow precipitation was correspondingly lower on its west slope. The tabular summit peaks then received proportionately less snow than now, and rose into regions of relative aridity. In that wintry epoch too, no doubt, the southwesterly winds went roaring over the crest of the range with greater fury than at the present time, and so, for both of these reasons, the conditions were peculiarly favorable for the non-glaciation of the higher wind-swept slopes. Paradoxical though it may sound, then, it is because of their great height that the tabular summit peaks and the little valley on Shepherd's Crest have remained unglaciated.

Remains the question: How old is the little valley on Shepherd's Crest? Or, more generally, how old is the "ancient landscape" of which it and the numerous tabular summit-tracts in the High Sierra are the remnants? Is it possible to determine its age in any way? Yes, it is possible, though only roughly and by roundabout methods.

It will be remembered that the Sierra Nevada consists essentially of a vast block of the earth's crust that lies tilted to the southwest, so that its eastern edge forms the crest line and its western edge lies deeply buried beneath the sediments in the great valley of California. This great earth-block gained its tilted attitude not at one bound but by successive hoists separated by long intervals of relative stability—intervals to be reckoned in millions of years. With each uplift the streams coursing down its west slope were tremendously accelerated and intrenched themselves in narrow steep-sided canyons. During each interval of repose their downward cutting slackened, the canyons widened out to valleys by the weathering and erosion of their sides, the tributary streams cut ramifying valleys, and there was developed a landscape or "erosion surface" with a topography of its own. Naturally the canyons and valleys of each new cycle of stream activity were cut into the topographic forms left by the preceding cycle, and so each new landscape was developed at the expense of the previous one.

On the west slope of the Sierra Nevada there can be distinguished four sets of topographic forms recording the work of as many cycles of stream erosion. The newest forms are the narrow V-shaped canyons in which the main streams now flow. They were carved in consequence of the last uptilting of the Sierra Block, which occurred probably early in the Pleistocene epoch.[8] Less than a million years old, they are still being actively deepened by the streams and remain youthful in aspect.

To a close observer it is patent that these Pleistocene canyons were cut into the broad floors of mature valleys of an earlier cycle. The Big Meadow flat, which lies more than 2000 feet above the Merced River at El Portal, is a remnant of such an older valley. The gently sloping platform about Turtleback Dome, over which the new highway to the Yosemite Valley is laid, is another remnant, and so is the entire Illilouette Valley, which has never been trenched. Examples are plentiful also along the other canyons of the Sierra Nevada, notably along those of the Stanislaus and San Joaquin. These older valleys, which attain great breadth on the lower slope of the range, are the products of a much longer cycle of erosion—a cycle that comprised probably all of the Pliocene epoch.

Big Meadow, Turtleback Dome, and the Illilouette Valley in their turn lie 2000 to 2500 feet below the general level of the little valleys on the uplands that flank the Yosemite. These billowy uplands are, indeed, portions of a still earlier landscape—a landscape that was produced during a very long cycle of erosion comprising most of the Miocene epoch and probably large parts of the preceding Oligocene epoch. Its age cannot be determined in the Yosemite region for want of telltale fossils, but it is indicated as probably late Miocene by fossils found near the old mining town of Columbia, north of the Tuolumne Table Mountain.

High above the Miocene landscape, which remains preserved on many of the extensive intercanyon tracts, stand the peaks and ranges that give the High Sierra its alpine character; and it is on some of the loftiest of these peaks and ranges, 2000 to 3000 feet above the Miocene hills, that are found the gently sloping, tabular remnants of the ancient landscape to which the little valley on Shepherd's Crest belongs. The age of this landscape is indicated approximately by the fact that in the northern parts of the Sierra Nevada remnants of it lie 1000 to nearly 2000 feet above the "fossil stream-beds" that contain the earlier gold-bearing gravel. These stream-beds, which were preserved by masses of indurated volcanic ash (rhyolite tuff), have yielded fossil plant remains of middle Eocene age. It follows that the ancient landscape in question goes back at least to early Eocene, possibly, even, to late Cretaceous time.

That any parts of a landscape so ancient could remain preserved in exposed

[8] See footnote on page 97, and Appendix.

mountaintops may at first seem incredible. Yet in the Sierra Nevada the fact is hardly open to doubt. Three circumstances, it would appear, have operated to preserve those bits of the early Eocene landscape that form the tabular summits of the highest peaks—namely, the resistant nature of the granitic rocks of which those peaks are made; the position of those peaks at the extreme heads of the rivers, where the streams are smallest and have the least cutting power; and their complete exemption from glacial erosion. Of course, it is not contended that these residual summit tracts have suffered no degradation whatever since early Eocene time; but the fact is stressed that they have suffered but very little change as compared with the deep canyons that surround them—so little, that they retain the gentle slopes and rounded contours that were imparted to them when the Sierra region still was a land of moderate elevation.

Of all the ancient summit-tracts in the High Sierra, certainly the little valley on Shepherd's Crest seems most remarkable; for a valley, being the pathway of a stream, is inherently more likely to be cut away during the uplift of a mountain range than is a ridge or a summit. Only some special circumstance could have saved it. Perhaps the streamlet on Shepherd's Crest was unable to compete with its neighbors because its water was entrapped by vertical fissures that developed across its path—the same fissures that separate the pinnacles of the south crest from one another. Again, the little valley seems remarkable because it has escaped glaciation, although valleys inherently afford good sites for glaciers. And, finally, to a student of the High Sierra it seems particularly precious because its non-glaciation, so well attested by its form, confirms the non-glaciation of many of the lofty tabular summits of the Sierra Nevada.

Reprinted from Sierra Club Bulletin, *1933, pages 68–80.*

Tuolumne Meadows, Yosemite. By Cedric Wright

TUOLUMNE MEADOWS
AND VICINITY

TUOLUMNE MEADOWS is situated in the midst of the broad Upper Tuolumne Basin, near the confluence of the Dana Fork and Lyell Fork of the Tuolumne River. During the glacial epoch two great ice streams, one coming from Mount Dana, the other from Mount Lyell, came together at the same spot. These two glaciers and a number of lesser ones that originated in the amphitheater-like hollows or "cirques" on the surrounding crests, filled the Upper Tuolumne Basin with ice to a depth of 2200 feet, as is clearly shown by the "ice lines" on Ragged Peak, to the north, and Johnson Peak, to the south. They created a "mer-de-glace" or ice sea 140 square miles in extent, the largest in the Sierra Nevada.

From this vast ice reservoir flowed the mighty Tuolumne Glacier, which was the longest and largest ice stream in the Sierra Nevada. It reached a maximum length of slightly over 60 miles and filled the Grand Canyon of the Tuolumne to the brim. At Pate Valley the Tuolumne Glacier attained the prodigious depth of 4500 feet, as is shown by the height of the moraines or debris ridges at the sides of the canyon.

In spite of its enormous size, however, the Tuolumne Glacier was unable to carry off the ice as fast as it accumulated in the Upper Tuolumne Basin. As a consequence overflows took place in different directions through gaps in the surrounding mountain crests. The largest volume escaped over the low, hummocky divide between Cathedral Peak and Tuolumne Peak and invaded the Tenaya Basin. It formed the bulk of the Tenaya Glacier, which was tributary to the Yosemite Glacier. Smaller outflows took place southwestward, over the Tuolumne Pass, southeastward over the Donohue Pass, eastward over the Mono Pass (into Bloody Canyon), and northeastward over the Tioga Pass.

As a result of its glacial history the Upper Tuolumne Basin is replete with features of unusual interest. On the rock floor, which is exposed to view in many places (notably along the lower course of the Dana Fork), grooves and striae produced by boulders and smaller rock fragments that were dragged by the ice, are abundant. Over large areas the granite still gleams with "glacier polish," imparted to it by the scouring of the fine rock powder carried by the glaciers. Boulders and blocks, large and small, torn from the mountain sides and dropped by the ice, as it melted, are strewn about here and there; and moraines or ridges of rock debris that accumulated along the margins of the glaciers occur in parallel series at the edges of the basin.

Of peculiar interest are those rocky knobs that were overridden by the glaciers, worn smooth and rounded on their upstream sides, but left more or less hackly on their downstream sides, where the ice plucked more than it ground. These asymmetric rock forms are known by the Swiss name of *roches moutonnées* (sheep-like rocks). Lembert Dome, which is about 500 feet high, exhibits this characteristic glacial form on a large scale. It was overwhelmed by the ice to a depth of 1500 feet. The most remarkable and highest rock monument of this type is Fairview Dome, which stands at the lower end of the Tuolumne Meadows. It might seem incredible that this sugarloaf dome, 1000 feet in height, was overtopped by the ice, yet such is clearly attested by its *roche moutonnée* form, by the patches of glacier polish on its crown, and by the height of the "ice line" on Cathedral Peak, which is 700 feet above its summit.

Moraine ridges are most numerous on the north side of the basin, especially in Moraine Flat. Dog Lake occupies a hollow between moraines. In its vicinity strips of meadow land frequently occur between parallel moraines marking successive stages in the melting down of the last glacier that filled the Tuolumne Basin. Terminal Moraines, such as are formed at the fronts of glaciers, occur nowhere except immediately in front of the small glaciers that still remain on some of the higher peaks. The explanation is, doubtless, that the ancient glaciers melted back rather steadily when the Ice Age drew to a close, and did not pause long enough at any point to build up a strong ridge of debris at their front.

Tuolumne Meadows is an excellent central base from which to make trips to the "living" glaciers that still remain on the high peaks round about. There are within the Tuolumne Basin and its immediate vicinity seven of these living glaciers—a greater number than is to be found in any other area of equal extent in the Sierra Nevada. They are of small size, it is true, and hardly comparable to the famous glaciers on Mount Rainier, or to those in the Swiss Alps or in

Alaska. The longest of them measure less than a mile in length, but they are nevertheless glaciers in the true sense of the term and not mere snow fields, for they are composed of hard, granular ice, they move slowly downhill with a slow flow-like motion, and they are broken by crevasses in consequence of their motion over irregular beds. Moreover, just as is the case with the large glaciers mentioned, so at the extreme head of each of these small glaciers there is between the ice and the rock of the mountain a gaping cleft (the *bergschrund* of Swiss mountaineers) that opens periodically as a result of the forward movement of the ice.

The largest ice body in the Tuolumne Basin lies on the north side of Mount Lyell. It is commonly known as the Lyell Glacier, but it consists in reality of two glaciers separated by a rocky spur. They might well be called the West Lyell and East Lyell glaciers. The ascent of Mount Lyell is usually made over the sloping surface of the West Lyell Glacier. The only obstacle that makes the climb difficult, especially in late summer, is the *bergschrund* at the head of the glacier.

A short distance farther west, on the north side of Mount Maclure, is the Maclure Glacier, a single, simple ice tongue, tapering downward to a blunt point, and enclosed by a massive moraine loop. Below the loop is a picturesque lakelet that reflects the glacier and the towering peak above.

Entirely different in character is the Dana Glacier, which occupies a deep cirque on the north side of Mount Dana. It is much broader than long, and, curiously, lies, not at the head of the cirque, which opens towards the northwest, but against its shady south wall. A moraine loop of great height encircles the ice front, showing that the glacier formerly was much larger and thicker than it is at present. The great volume of morainal material is accounted for by the fact that the ancient volcanic rocks of which Mount Dana is largely made break up rather readily under the repeated attacks of frost—more readily than the relatively massive granites that prevail throughout the High Sierra.

Two small glaciers lie tucked away under the north slopes of Kuna Peak and Koip Peak. They are readily reached from the trail that leads over the Parker Pass. Of much larger size is the Conness Glacier, which occupies a sheer-walled cirque on the northeast side of Mount Conness. Like the Dana, Kuna, and Koip glaciers, the Conness is much broader than long. It measures about three-fourths of a mile in breadth and a quarter of a mile in length. From the summit of Mount Conness one looks down upon the entire expanse of ice, but to reach the foot of the glacier one must go by way of the Tioga Pass and the Saddlebag Lakes.

Measurements by the National Park Service are being made annually to the fronts of all the glaciers described for the purpose of determining the extent to which they have advanced or melted back. This work is being done as a part of a general plan of glacier measurements throughout the western United States and Alaska that was put into operation a few years ago by the Committee on Glaciers of the Geophysical Union (Branch of the National Research Council in Washington). The principal object is to obtain systematic records of the advance or recession of the glaciers that will indicate the trend of climatic changes now in progress.

All of the glaciers in the Sierra Nevada have been melting back more or less constantly ever since the seventies of the last century. The little glacier which John Muir discovered in 1871 (on the Clark Range) has melted away entirely, and a host of small cirque glaciers of the same type doubtless have vanished from the range within the last fifty years.

The features of the Upper Tuolumne Basin are carved very largely from granite, a material of igneous origin that welled up in a molten state and crystallized into hard rock as it cooled. It was not, however, lava properly speaking, for it did not flow out upon the surface of the earth. It occupied vast subterranean chambers beneath the buckled and broken strata of an ancient mountain system that stood on the site of the present Sierra Nevada more than a hundred million years ago.

The reason why the granite is now exposed at the surface throughout the Upper Tuolumne Basin, and indeed throughout a large part of the Sierra Nevada, is that the ancient mountains that covered it have been completely worn down, the rocks as they weathered and disintegrated, being removed, fragment by fragment, grain by grain, by washing rains and the running water of brooks and rivers.

The granite peculiar to the Upper Tuolumne Basin is known as Cathedral Peak granite and is readily distinguished from the other types of granite in the Sierra Nevada (which represent different upflows of molten material) by the large, approximately rectangular crystals of whitish feldspar which it contains. In the ice-polished rock floors these crystals, which measure from one to two inches in length, resemble lumps of domino sugar disseminated through a buff or pinkish groundmass.

Of the older rocks that originally overlay the granite and made up the bulk of the ancient mountains just referred to, considerable masses remain on the peaks surrounding the Upper Tuolumne Basin, notably on Mount Dana, Mount Gibbs, Parker Peak, Koip Peak and Blacktop; likewise on Parsons Peak and Simmons Peak, and in a narrow belt extending along the northeast slopes of

Cathedral Peak, Yosemite. By Philip Hyde

Mount Maclure and Mount Lyell. Their strata, which originally were flatlying, in many places now stand vertical or nearly so, and elsewhere appear buckled and folded in various ways. It is in this buckling and folding of the strata that geologists find evidence of the former existence of a mountain system that antedated the present Sierra Nevada.

As a result of the intense pressure to which they were subjected when the ancient mountains were formed, the rocks were greatly altered in consistency, indurated and rendered crystalline—they were metamorphosed, as geologists say, and they are therefore properly referred to as *metamorphic* rocks. Among them were originally sandstones, shales, and limestones of marine origin. The sandstones have become quartzites; the shales, schists; and the limestone, marble.

There were, however, also large masses of lava and other volcanic rocks, and these have become metamorphosed into peculiar schistose rocks of various types. Such metamorphic lavas abound at the foot of Mount Lyell and on Mount Dana. They are readily recognized by their mottled appearance, the steam cavities or vesicles in the lavas having been filled with light colored minerals that contrast with the somber hue of the rocks themselves.

All the metamorphic rocks except the marble (of which there is but little in the High Sierra) are dark in general tone as compared with the granites. The mountains of which they are composed consequently have a dusky appearance in the landscape, alongside of the bright, granitic peaks—they seem overcast by perpetual cloud shadows.

One of several essays written by Dr. Matthes in the middle '30's at the request of the Yosemite Park and Curry Company in connection with the plan, initiated as early as 1923, to establish lodgings for the use of hikers from Yosemite Valley who wished to make overnight excursions into the high country. The history of these lodgings, known first as "Hikers' Camps" and later as "High Sierra Camps," has been told by Dr. Carl P. Russell (One Hundred Years in Yosemite: The Story of a Great Park and Its Friends, *1947 edition, pages 113–115). Though widely used in typewritten form, so far as known the essays were never printed.*

THE SCENERY ABOUT
TENAYA LAKE

TENAYA LAKE lies, like a sapphire gem, ensconced in the bosom of the Tenaya Basin, near the headwaters of the stream that dashes down rugged Tenaya Canyon. The lake is situated at an altitude of 8141 feet, somewhat more than 4000 feet above the level of the Yosemite Valley, and is surrounded by peaks of massive and imposing sculpture that rise to elevations between 10,000 and 11,000 feet. To the visitor who comes up from the valley by the Tenaya Lake Trail or the Tioga Road, the Tenaya Basin is the first bit of real High Sierra, fascinating both by reason of its scenic aspect and because of the extraordinarily vivid evidences of glacial action that appear on every hand.

On the west and northwest sides the basin is enclosed by Mount Hoffmann (10,836) and Tuolumne Peak (10,875) which form really a continuous range. On the northeast side stands sharp-spired Cathedral Peak (10,933); overlooking the lake from the east is blunt sheerwalled Tenaya Peak (10,300), and beyond it loom the clustered pinnacles of the Echo Peaks (11,000).

Directly from the north shore of the lake rises a smaller, roundish mountain of massive and almost wholly bare granite, which is known as Polly Dome (9786). It deserves more attention than is usually bestowed upon it, for its smoothed and in part polished sides and crown proclaim the fact that the glaciers of the Ice Age have repeatedly overwhelmed it. There are even glacial lakelets perched high up on its slopes. Polly Dome stands 1645 feet above Tenaya Lake, and so it is evident that the ice here attained a depth of more than 1600 feet.

To one not familiar with the details of glacial action in the High Sierra it might seem well nigh incredible that the ice could have attained so great a depth in the Tenaya Basin, yet Polly Dome does not even afford the full measure. Tenaya Peak, which rises 2160 feet above the lake, also was overswept, as is clearly proved by its ice-smoothed summit and the "erratic" boulders that are scattered upon it. To find the highest level attained by the glaciers one must go to the base of the pinnacles of the Echo Peaks or the neighboring crest of Columbia Finger. The frail, splintered forms of those pinnacles show that they have never been overridden by the ice, while the smoothly rounded mountains which they surmount have clearly been abraded. The *ice line* lies fully 2460 feet above Tenaya Lake.

Where did these vast quantities of ice originate, you may ask? The great bulk of it came from the upper Tuolumne Basin, of which the Tuolumne Meadows are now the central feature. That basin was formerly an immense ice reservoir, the largest of its kind in the High Sierra. Into it flowed dozens of sluggish ice streams from the amphitheater-like hollows or "cirques" on the sides of Mount Lyell, Mount Maclure, Kuna Crest, Mount Dana, and the other peaks round about. From it issued the mighty Tuolumne Glacier, which reached a length of 60 miles and was the largest ice stream in the Sierra Nevada. This great trunk glacier, nevertheless, was unable to carry off the ice as fast as it accumulated, and as a consequence the level of the ice sea rose until at last overflow took place in various directions through gaps and saddles between the peaks. By far the largest amount spilled over the hummocky divide that separates the Tuolumne Basin from the Tenaya Basin. It was a flow four miles wide, between Cathedral Peak and Tuolumne Peak. This ice flow invaded the Tenaya Basin, where its volume was augmented by local ice streams that issued from cirques on Cathedral and Tenaya peaks, Sunrise Mountain, and Mt. Hoffmann.

So abundant was the ice in the basin that the outflowing Tenaya Glacier, although 2500 feet thick, was unable to draw off all of it, and as a consequence a broad ice sheet spread over the rugged upland north of Tenaya Canyon, as far west as Porcupine Flat. Even Mount Watkins, which as viewed from Mirror Lake seems like another El Capitan, was completely overwhelmed. This fact is attested by several huge ice-borne boulders that lie on its bald, rounded summit (which, by the way, is easily accessible and well worthy of a visit).

In the central portion of the Tenaya Basin the eroding action of the ice was most vigorous, and there, consequently, only a sprinkling of boulders was left on the rock floors; but at the margins the rock debris was piled up in ridges or "moraines." These are most numerous on the south side of the basin, where the Forsyth Trail comes down. They extend approximately parallel to one another, in concentric curves.

Naturally the Tenaya Basin exhibits in practically all its features the effects of the intense erosive action of the ancient ice floods. Tenaya Lake, its central feature, occupies a hollow that was literally gouged out in its rock floor. The lake has a sounded depth of 114 feet. Not all this depth is to be accredited to glacial excavation, however, for at its lower end the lake is enclosed by glacial and stream-borne rock debris of unknown thickness. In that

Tenaya Lake, Yosemite. By Ansel Adams

respect Tenaya Lake is closely analagous to the much larger body of water which at the end of the Ice Age filled the bottom of the Yosemite Valley. Ancient Lake Yosemite lay in a glacially excavated rock basin five and a half miles long, but its outlet was across a moraine which raised the level of the water somewhat. Ancient Lake Yosemite has long since been filled with gravel and sand dumped into it by the Merced River and Tenaya Creek, and is now replaced by a level floor—the beautiful parklike tract on which most of the tourist camps are pitched. Tenaya Lake likewise will be filled some day, but that time is still far off, for the only two streamlets that enter it carry but little sand.

The filling is accomplished not by the settling of sediment in layers over the entire lake bottom, but by the forward growth of the deltas which the streamlets are building at their mouths. The extent to which these deltas already have encroached upon the lake is shown by the stretches of low sandy ground covered with willows and pines at the mouths of the streams. So extremely slow is the rate of advance of the delta that the waves stirred up by the daily southwest winds have no difficulty in keeping its front trimmed to a smooth curve.

At the Foot of Tenaya Lake is a feature of a relatively rare type that deserves a word of explanation. The shore there is raised to the form of a low, hummocky ridge crowned with glacial boulders. This ridge is only from one foot to three feet high above the level land immediately back of it, and is so unobtrusive that it might readily be overlooked. Similar hummocky ridges occur along the shores of a number of other lakes in the High Sierra—notably Ireland Lake—and also of many lakes in Wisconsin and Minnesota. For a long time the origin of such ridges was in doubt, but it is now known from actual observation that they are built of material that is literally shoved out of the lakes by the ice that forms on them in winter. These ridges are therefore appropriately known as "ice ramparts."

An ice rampart is formed, in brief, as follows. The ice that freezes on a lake, although seemingly inert and unchanging, in reality contracts and expands appreciably with variations in the daily temperature. During a cold spell, with temperatures well below zero, the ice contracts sharply, and if it can not pull away from the shore becomes rent by open fissures. Water at once fills these fissures and, upon coming into contact with the cold air, freezes in them, thereby reuniting the sheet, which now fits snugly in the lake basin. With the next warm spell the ice again expands and as a consequence it pushes with great force against the shores. Either the ice breaks a short distance from shore and piles up in a pressure ridge, or its marginal portion is shoved bodily up on the land, carrying with it the rocks and mud that are frozen in it. The latter action may be repeated several times during a winter, and so in the course of time the lake bottom for some distance out from the shore is cleared and smoothed, and the material shoved up on the shore is piled together in a low, jumbled ridge. The tremendous force that is exerted by the ice in this apparently insignificant process is strikingly attested at Tenaya Lake by the large size of the boulders in and on the ice rampart.

To return to the evidences of glacial erosion in the Tenaya Basin: The walls, the slopes, and the floors of solid granite almost everywhere are abraded to smooth-flowing curves. Over considerable areas they still retain the polish, striae, and grooves that were imparted to them by the rock fragments held by the slow-moving ice mass. Indeed, next to the upper Merced Basin the Tenaya Basin offers the most impressive exhibit of glacially-worn rock that is readily accessible in the High Sierra. Some of the polished and gleaming granite is to be seen from the automobile road, especially along the shore of Tenaya Lake. Highly appropriate was the old Indian name for the lake—Py-we-ack, meaning the "water of shining rocks." (The name Tenaya was given to it by the historic Mariposa Battalion, the first group of white men to set foot in the Yosemite Valley, in 1851, in memory of Chief Tenaya, of the Yosemite Indians, whom they captured at the lake.)

Glacier polish is, even to the casual observer, an intensely fascinating thing, for it attests most vividly the grinding power of the ancient glaciers and by reason of its good state of preservation over large areas impresses one with the relative recency of the Ice Age. The fact is that glacier polish, because of its very smoothness, acts somewhat as a protective coating that retards the weathering of the rock. It permits water to run off more promptly than it would from a rough surface, and thereby lessens the proportionate amount that soaks into the rock. And this, again, retards the growth of mosses and lichens from whose decay are derived the acids that decompose the weaker minerals. It is a notable fact, that may be observed in many places in the High Sierra, that wherever the glacier polish finally scales off rock weathering is at once resumed at a relatively rapid rate (the normal rate).

The gleaming polish itself is produced, of course, by abrasion with the fine rock powder which the glacier carries in its lower layers. Far more impressive, as regards the pressure which the ice mass exerted on its bed, is the testimony of the grooves and striae. They show that the force was sufficient to cause angular blocks dragged by the glacier to furrow sound, unweathered granite to depths of a quarter or even a half inch, and to cause individual rock grains (of quartz, presumably) to leave tiny furrows (striae) of their own.

The pressure can be calculated from the known thickness attained by the ice. Since a column of glacier ice 1000 feet high weighs about 30 tons per square foot, the pressure on the rock floors about Tenaya Lake at the time of maximum glaciation (when the ice was about 2400 feet thick) must have been about 74 tons per square foot. And to this must be added the forward thrust due to the gravitation of the ice mass. Much of the grooving and scratching, however, must have been done with less pressure than that stated, for many of the prominent grooves are still rough and fresh looking, from which circumstance it is evident

Glacier polish and striae on aplite. Blocks disrupted by postglacial frost work.
By François Matthes

that they were made but a short time before the ice melted. Were they older, they would now appear smoothed and polished.

One factor that accounts for the unusually fine display of polish, grooves, and other glacial markings in the Tenaya Basin is that the granite there is very massive—that is, it is broken by joint fractures only at long intervals. Normally granite is jointed at intervals of a few feet. The partings run in parallel sets, and there are three or more different sets that intersect one another at various angles so as to divide the rock into angular blocks and slabs. Wherever the rock is so divided glacier polish is apt to be scarce, for the glacier, instead of merely grinding, quarries out the blocks and slabs. The Yosemite Valley was quarried out in this fashion, and its walls in consequence are for the most part hackled and faceted, and bear glacier polish only in a few spots. But in the Tenaya Basin the joints are often scores and even hundreds of feet apart, so that the glacier could not quarry but only grind and polish the surface of the

Glacier polish, head of Tenaya Canyon. By David Brower

rock. Such abrasion is of course a much slower process than quarrying, especially in hard and tough granite. The smoothed and polished walls and floor of the Tenaya Basin, therefore, show, if anything, that the glacier there excavated with great difficulty and accomplished relatively small results.

In the Tenaya Basin curving shells due to exfoliation are to be seen in many places, but they are not plentiful because the most of those that were loosened were quarried away by the glaciers, and sufficient time has not elapsed since the end of the Ice Age for the production of any new shells. In a general way, therefore, the smoothly curving, billowy rock forms of the Tenaya Basin have been fashioned in part by exfoliation and in part by glacial action.

Of the older rocks that formerly roofed over the granite a few remnants still exist in the vicinity of May Lake. The ridge that encloses the lake basin on the east side consists in part of brown quartzite and white marble, and the slope of Mount Hoffmann immediately above the lake is composed of similar materials. The quartzite is an ancient sandstone that was altered and made crystalline by the intense pressure and heat to which it was subjected when the strata were folded as the earlier mountain system arose. The marble was produced by the same process from limestone. The sandstone originated probably as sand on the shore of the continent, and the limestone was built up as a reef by corals and algae in a shallow sea.

It may seem surprising that these remnants of quartzite and marble occur at the base of Mount Hoffmann and not on its summit, which consists of pure granite. The explanation is that a large body of these metamorphic rocks hung down from the roof into the fluid granite, forming a dividing wall between two upwelling masses. Of that wall only the lower portions remain, the upper portions having long since been destroyed together with the roof. Many similar instances occur in different places in the Sierra Nevada. Among the most spectacular is a mass of contorted strata that hangs on the northwest slope of Tuolumne Peak.

See note on page 128.

MERCED LAKE

AND ITS ENVIRONMENT

THE UPPER Merced Canyon, in which Merced Lake is situated, may well be termed a lesser Yosemite, still unfinished. Like the main Yosemite Valley it is broadly U-shaped and has imposing walls of granite and waterfalls that leap down from lofty side valleys, but its floor is for the most part still unmade.

The level, parklike floor of the main Yosemite, which adds so much to the charm and livableness of that valley, was formed by the filling of a glacially excavated lake basin with sand and gravel brought down by the Merced River and Tenaya Creek. Those materials were not spread in layers on the floor of the basin but were deposited at the head of the lake in fan-shaped deltas, one at the mouth of each stream. The two deltas grew forward until they coalesced, and then a single large delta, built jointly by the two streams, advanced steadily until in the course of thousands of years it reached the lower end of the basin. As the late David Curry used to express it in his campfire talks: When the delta bumped its nose against the moraine at the foot of the lake, the filling was completed.

Merced Lake, though of much smaller dimensions, is the counterpart of ancient Lake Yosemite, except that it has no morainal dam at its lower end. It occupies a basin that was excavated in the rock floor of the canyon by the powerful Merced Glacier. Soundings have shown the basin to be about 80 feet deep. At the head of the lake the Merced River is even now building a delta of sand and gravel, and that delta, as it grows forward, will ultimately fill the lake and replace it with a level floor. The Sierra Nevada will then have gained one more Yosemite. But that event lies far in the future, for the delta front is advancing at an extremely slow rate—so slowly that the vegetation is amply able to keep up with its progress. Grass grows right up to the edge of the beach; willows and bushes follow within a few yards; and the forest trees are not far behind. Indeed, there is no danger that beautiful Lake Merced will diminish appreciably in size within our time or even in centuries to come.

That the lake lies really in a rock bowl and has no other kind of barrier is evident from the nature of its outlet. There the water slips out over a smooth barrier of extremely massive granite. So far apart are the fractures or "joints"

View diagonally across Merced Lake, showing exfoliating cliffs on the south side, the forested delta of the river at the head of the lake, and part of the Merced Canyon above. Yosemite National Park, California. By François Matthes

in that rock mass that the Merced Glacier could only grind—"sand paper" its surface. The lake basin, on the other hand, was excavated in a place where the rock was cut by many intersecting joints, so that it could be "quarried" out in blocks by the moving ice. Wherever the joint structure of the granite in the Sierra Nevada permitted the glaciers to quarry out blocks on a large scale, the canyons were profoundly modified by glaciation; but wherever the granite was massive, so that glaciers could only grind, the changes effected were relatively small.

Washburn Lake, which lies 3 miles up valley from Merced Lake, is also a typical glacial lake occupying a rock basin enclosed by a barrier of massive granite. It has a sounded depth of 86 feet, but at its outlet the water is hardly two feet deep. The rock barrier is in plain view from the foot bridge that spans the outlet. Washburn Lake also has a delta at its head and already has lost about 500 feet of its original length by the forward growth of that delta.

It may seem strange that Merced Lake and Washburn Lake, though less than a mile long each, are still so largely unfilled, whereas ancient Lake Yosemite, which measured five and a half miles in length and probably at least 200 feet in depth, has been extinct for a long time. The reason is, in the main, that during the last glacial epoch the glaciers made two major advances separated by a long interval. Only the first advance penetrated the Yosemite Valley, while the second reached no farther than to the mouth of the Little Yosemite. The filling of Lake Yosemite therefore began many thousand years before Merced Lake and Washburn Lake were uncovered by the slowly melting ice. A second reason is that the Merced River and Tenaya Creek for a long time poured into Lake Yosemite large quantities of rock debris derived from the still extensive and active glaciers in the High Sierra, whereas the Merced River in its headwater reaches naturally carried only a small load.

Many other glacial lakes and lakelets in the upper Merced Basin are accessible from Merced Lake. Some of the most picturesque lie on the broad rock benches at the base of Merced Peak, Ottoway Peak, and Red Peak. Others lie strung like turquoise beads in the high-level canyon of the Lyell Fork and in the vicinity of the Isberg Pass. These are readily reached from the Isberg Pass Trail.

Of particular interest is Babcock Lake, which lies tucked away in a recess, two miles to the northeast of Merced Lake and nearly 2000 feet above it. In that recess the glacier that came southward from the twin valleys of Emerick and Fletcher creeks was deflected abruptly toward the east and at the turn developed tremendous excavating power. The granite there being traversed by rather widely spaced but strongly developed master joints, the glacier tore out great rectangular blocks and slabs, leaving the basin with remarkably straight sides, so that it now looks as if it had been sawed out with a cyclopean saw.

The depth which the Merced Glacier attained in the neighborhood of Merced Lake is indicated by the height of the lateral moraines (ridges of rock debris) which it left on the shoulders of the canyon. These moraines lie fully 2200 feet above Merced Lake and Washburn Lake. Those on the northeast side of the canyon are readily inspected from the Isberg Pass Trail, which parallels them for miles. As the canyon has suffered no further deepening since these moraines were laid down, there can be no doubt that the ice was about 2200 feet thick. When glacial conditions reached an optimum it probably was even somewhat thicker. The pressure which the Merced Glacier exerted upon its bed, due to its weight alone, must therefore have been fully 66 tons to the square foot. Added to that was the powerful forward thrust due to the gravitation of the ice mass and to the pressure of the many tributary glaciers that converged upon it from many different directions. The sum total of the Merced Glacier's energy in the canyon must therefore have been very great, and the depth of the lake basins is thus readily accounted for.

Other evidences of the tremendous pressure which the Merced Glacier exerted upon its bed are to be seen in the grooves, striae, and polish which abound on the rock floor of the canyon. These fascinating products of glacial action are displayed in the vicinity of Merced Lake on an unusually grand scale, because of the prevalence of massive granite. The most impressive exhibits are along the old trail below Merced Lake, which is laid over the bare rock for long distances. The trail there is indicated by a row of stones, there being no other way of marking it across the featureless flats. Elsewhere in the Sierra Nevada, and in most other glaciated mountains, one may see glacier polish by the square yard, but here one beholds it literally by the acre. Even the walls of the canyon gleam with glacier polish up to a great height.

The polish was imparted to the granite by the fine rock dust which the grinding glacier carried in its bottom layers. The striae were produced by small angular fragments of hard rock, mostly quartz, and the grooves by large, heavy blocks that were dragged along by the slow-moving ice stream. Some of the grooves are from a quarter inch to a half inch in depth—truly amazing depths considering how hard and tough fresh, unweathered granite is.

Most amazing are the slanting grooves to be seen on the steep rock face to the north of the outlet of Merced Lake. There the ice rode up at a high angle to surmount a rock spur that projected into its channel. The grooves consequently slant upward, not downward, in the direction in which the ice moved. During the middle of the day these slanting grooves are inconspicuous, but in the early forenoon they stand out very prominently and are readily photographed.

Associated with the grooves, in many places on the floor of the canyon, are two kinds of curving fractures in the granite that afford impressive testimony of the glacier's disrupting power. These are known as *chatter marks* and *crescentic gouges*. The chatter marks are the most abundant. They are fine cracks that are bowed upvalleyward and have a spread ranging from a few inches to a foot or more. They occur in series, spaced a fraction of an inch apart, each series astride of a more or less distinct groove. It is evident that they are tension cracks produced by the terrific pull exerted by the dragged boulders. Naturally they are most abundant in the more brittle kinds of rock, such as the aplite, a fine grained, cream colored rock that cuts across the granite here and there in so-called "dikes." In some localities chatter marks are confined wholly to the aplite, dying out in the neighboring granite, which is tougher.

The crescentic gouges are bowed downvalleyward and although relatively uncommon, are very conspicuous wherever they do occur. They also are arranged in series, but there are seldom more than four or five in any one series, and they are spaced several inches or even more than a foot apart. They resemble the hoof marks of a gigantic horse—a horse that strode down the valley, stubbing its toes with terrific force so as to spall off flakes from the rock floor. These flakes were thickest at the outer curve and thinned inward to a knife edge. That the gouges are due to great pressure can not be doubted, but the precise manner in which they were made still remains a mystery.

A word about the origin of the granite, which is the prevailing country rock throughout the High Sierra. It is a material that welled up in a molten state from the depths of the earth and crystallized as it cooled. It did not, however, flow out upon the surface of the earth like lava, but remained confined in vast subterranean chambers beneath the outer crust. In the Sierra Nevada this crust consisted of strata of slate, schist, quartzite, and marble—the same materials that are still visible in the Merced Canyon below El Portal. These strata, originally flat lying, were buckled into huge wrinkles so as to give rise to a system of parallel mountain ridges with northwesterly trend. Those mountain ridges stood on the site of the present Sierra Nevada more than a hundred million years ago, but in the course of time they were completely worn away, their rocks, as they weathered and disintegrated, being carried away fragment by fragment, grain by grain, largely by washing rains and by brooks and rivers. Probably not less than two miles of rock have thus been removed by what geologists term the processes of erosion, and so the granite has been laid bare over large areas.

There were many upwellings of this molten material and as a consequence there are now many different types of granite in the Sierra Nevada. Two types occur in the upper Merced Basin—the Half Dome "quartz monzonite" and the Cathedral Peak granite. The former, named for Half Dome, makes up the lower part of the basin and all of the Little Yosemite region. The latter occurs chiefly in the Cathedral Range and in the country about the Tuolumne Meadows.

The two rocks are readily distinguished from each other by the fact that the Half Dome granite is even textured, whereas the Cathedral Peak granite contains unusually large crystals of white or pinkish feldspar—about two inches in length and approximately rectangular in outline. As the granite disintegrates these large feldspar crystals are liberated and remain lying on the ground. Quantities of them may be picked up along the trail to the Tuolumne Pass and

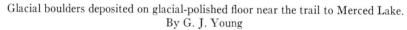

Glacial boulders deposited on glacial-polished floor near the trail to Merced Lake.
By G. J. Young

also along the Isberg Pass Trail. In the glacially-polished rock floors these crystals lie embedded as in a mosaic—they remind one of lumps of domino sugar.

Of the older rocks that formerly overlay the granite and made up the bulk of the ancient mountain ranges already referred to, a few small patches remain on the peaks surrounding the upper Merced Basin. Of greatest interest, perhaps, is the mass of yellowish quartzite that is situated on the north spur of Mount Clark, east of Clark Canyon. This quartzite is an ancient sandstone that was altered—metamorphosed, as geologists say—by the intense pressure and heat to which it was subjected when the ancient mountains were created by the buckling and folding of their strata.

The massive granite in the upper Merced Canyon on which the glacier polish is so extensively preserved is all of it Half Dome granite. Indeed, this granite excels among the many different types of granitic rock in the Sierra Nevada by its remarkably massive structure. As a rule granitic rocks are traversed by many natural partings, or joints, as they are called, that develop while the mass was solidifying. Additional fractures may be produced later

The domes of the Merced Canyon—like those elsewhere in Yosemite—owe their smoothly rounded forms to long-continued exfoliation, many successive shells having been cast off from their bodies in the course of time. By G. J. Young

by stresses within the crust of the earth. Commonly the joints occur in parallel sets, spaced from one foot to several feet apart, and three or more such sets of joints intersect one another so as to divide the rock into angular blocks and slabs. But in the Half Dome granite not infrequently joints are wholly absent over distances of hundreds and even thousands of feet, horizontally and vertically. Such is notably the case in Half Dome itself, which consists essentially of a single, huge monolith. Most of the great cliffs of the Little Yosemite, of Lost Valley, and along the upper Merced Canyon are likewise composed of enormous masses of unfractured rock. The few master joints that traverse them are all the more prominent because of their isolation. Only in those joints can the vegetation find a root hold, and it is for that reason that the smooth cliffs, rock floors and rock terraces in the upper Merced Canyon are largely bare.

In reality this massive granite has not always been without fractures. The numerous dikes of aplite that traverse it in various directions show that it was once broken by many fissures. But into those fissures the hot, liquid aplite shot up and, as it crystallized, it sealed them tightly, uniting all the great fragments again into one solid, continuous mass. All along the upper Merced Canyon aplite dikes abound. They are readily recognized by their creamy or light buff color, which contrasts with the darker hue of the speckled granite. Some of them stand out slightly above the surface of the granite, because of their superior resistance to the weather. The dikes vary in width from a few inches to several feet; they even taper down to mere threads, showing that the molten aplite was an extremely fluid substance that could penetrate into the finest cracks.

In some places there are two sets of dikes, one cut through by the other. Frequently in such cases the older dikes appear offset by a few inches or even a foot, the great blocks of granite having been moved and dislocated. There is a certain fascination in the thought that by a little patient study one can today ascertain in some detail what manner of processes went on at a depth of two miles beneath the surface of the earth—under a mountain system that is no longer in existence—more than a hundred million years ago.

A peculiar feature of massive granite is that it tends to cast off thick, curving shells or plates from its surface. Such curving shells are to be seen on all the great domes of the Yosemite region, and on the walls of the Little Yosemite and the upper Merced Canyon. The explanation in all probability is that the granite, having crystallized under tremendous pressure, beneath miles of superincumbent rock, tends to expand when freed from its load. In normally jointed granite the expansion is accommodated by slight movements on the intersecting fractures, but in massive granite it results in the bursting off of shells or plates approximately parallel to the exposed surface. Geologists term this process "exfoliation."

The domes of the Yosemite region unquestionably owe their smoothly rounded forms to long-continued exfoliation, many successive shells having been cast off from their bodies in the course of time. It was believed formerly that the domes had been rounded by overriding glaciers; but that is now realized to be a fallacy, for some of the most typical domes—notably Sentinel and Half Dome—were never overtopped by the ice, as is now positively known from a detailed survey of the glacial moraines. The lower domes were over-ridden, but they are no rounder than the higher unglaciated ones.

Dome-like rock forms and smoothly curved cliffs predominate throughout the Little Yosemite, Lost Valley, and the upper Merced Canyon. They are to be interpreted as having been shaped in part by exfoliation, in part by glacial grinding. Doubtless all of them were heavily covered with shells before the Ice Age began. The old preglacial shells were, however, all plucked off during the first stage of glaciation, and the granite cores were probably ground and reshaped by the ice. Then, during the ensuing interglacial stage, exfoliation again proceeded undisturbed. The newly-formed shells were again removed during the next glacial stage; and so the two processes worked in alternation throughout the Ice Age, which in the Sierra Nevada comprised at least three stages of glaciation.

The rock forms as they now appear are still substantially as they were molded by the last glaciers. Over large areas, in fact, no new shells have been produced in all the time that has elapsed since the end of the Ice Age. When it is realized that that interval in the High Sierra was probably between 10,000 and 20,000 years long, the extreme slowness of the exfoliation process will be apparent.

See note on page 128.

The Watchtower, Tokopah Valley, Sequoia National Park, California.
Courtesy George Mauger, Sequoia and Kings Canyon National Parks Company

LODGEPOLE CAMP AND
TOKOPAH VALLEY

LODGEPOLE CAMP is situated at an elevation of more than 6700 feet in what is properly termed the middle course of the Marble Fork Canyon. Tokopah Valley, which lies immediately upstream from it, is really its continuation, still in a pristine state of lovely wildness. Tokopah differs from Lodgepole chiefly in that it is flanked by towering cliffs instead of forested slopes. Both have broad and in places nearly level floors and are particularly inviting by reason of their charming groves of pine and fir and the pleasing alternations of pools, cascades, and riffles in the stream.

Below, from the highway bridge down to the junction with the Middle Fork of the Kaweah, is the lower canyon, through which the Marble Fork makes a tumultuous descent, falling as much as 1000 feet in a single mile, and dropping a total of 4800 feet. It is an extremely rugged canyon that attains a maximum depth of 3000 feet, west of the Giant Forest, and in some stretches is utterly impassable, even to the boldest mountaineer. It is so notably at the Marble Falls, where the river is actively cutting its channel across great upstanding beds of white and bluish marble—whence the name Marble Fork.

Above Tokopah Valley—that is, above the 1300-foot cliffs over which the Tokopah Falls descend—is the upper canyon, which again differs wholly in character from the middle and lower canyons. It is a broadly open basin, flanked by mountains of great height—Mount Silliman (11,188) on the north, and Alta Peak (11,211) on the south, and enclosed at its head by a lofty plateau, known as the Tableland, 11,300 feet in altitude. Its most remarkable characteristic is its barrenness. It presents a vast expanse of smooth, bare granite, from which all soil and vegetation have been removed. There are, it is true, a few groves of lodgepole pine and fir in its lower portion, but these seem, in a comprehensive view such as may be obtained from the Watchtower,

147

merely dark, wooded islands in a dazzling, billowy sea of granite. The river
there has but a shallow channel and races, white with foam, over the smooth,
but scaling rock.

Why, it may be asked, are the lower, middle and upper portions of the
Marble Fork Canyon so entirely unlike in form and aspect, and how does it
come that Lodgepole and Tokopah in the middle course are so lovely and
attractive, from man's point of view, whereas the lower and upper canyons,
though scenically impressive and in some respects amazing, are rather lacking
in attractive qualities?

First of all it should be explained that the steep lower canyon is a much
younger, more recently carved feature of the landscape than the middle and
upper canyons. It was cut by the river, and is still in process of being cut, in
consequence of a great uplift that added several thousand feet to the height
of the Sierra Nevada, and steepened the river's course, thereby accelerating
its flow and increasing its cutting or eroding power. The middle and upper
canyons, on the other hand, are relatively ancient features dating back to the
period that preceded the great uplift, when the Sierra still had only moderate
height. Lodgepole and Tokopah have not yet been reached by the vigorous
canyon cutting below, which is proceeding from the foothills upward.

The Giant Forest, it may be remarked incidentally, stands on a portion of
the same ancient landscape to which Lodgepole and Tokopah belong. The
lower Marble Canyon has been trenched deeply beneath its surface, and so has
the great canyon of the Middle Fork, and as a result the Giant Forest now
stands on an elevated plateau. From the southern edge of that plateau, which
has an altitude of about 6500 feet, to the channel of the Middle Fork below
there is a drop of fully 4000 feet.

The plateau on which the Giant Forest stands is, however, by no means
the highest part of the region, for above it rises Alta Peak, 11,211 feet in height.
That peak, moreover, is merely the culminating point of a ridge about 1½
miles in length that connects at the northeast by a shallow saddle with the
Tableland. And the Tableland itself is without doubt a large remnant of a
landscape far more ancient still than that on which the Giant Forest stands,
indeed many millions of years more ancient. It antedates an earlier uplift of
the range as a result of which the Marble Fork cut its course down to the level
of Lodgepole Valley and the Giant Forest plateau. Small remnants of that
very ancient landscape, or erosion surface, as geologists would call it, exist

Tokopah Falls on the Marble Fork of the Kaweah River, Sequoia.
Courtesy George Mauger, Sequoia and Kings Canyon National Parks Company

on a number of the higher peaks of the Sierra Nevada, notably on Mount Whitney, Mount Langley and Table Mountain on the Great Western Divide. There are thus indicated in the features of the range two distinct periods of uplift and consequent canyon cutting.

In this connection it may be explained that the Sierra Nevada, taken as a whole, is essentially one huge block of the crust of the earth, 430 miles long, that lies in a tilted position with its eastern edge upraised so as to form the crest line. Measured from the crest line to the western foothills the block is 40 to 80 miles broad, but as its surface dips under the silts that fill the Great

Valley of California and probably continues beneath them for many miles more, the total breadth of the Sierra block may be considerably over 100 miles. That the Sierra Nevada is actually a tilted crust block, as here described, had long been recognized by geologists, but the history of the successive uplifts by which it has gained its great altitude was not known until the geologic history of the Yosemite Valley was worked out, in 1913 and 1914.

To return to Lodgepole and Tokopah, these portions of the middle course of the Marble Fork Canyon, though undoubtedly forming part of the ancient landscape on which the Giant Forest stands, nevertheless now present a very different appearance from that which was given them by the river. For during the Ice Age, which followed upon the last great uplift, they became the pathway of a glacier and for many thousand years were subjected to its excavating and remodeling action. That glacier originated on the Tableland, which was completely covered by ice, as is still clearly shown by the glacier polish and scratches on its surface; and it was reinforced by a number of short tributary glaciers that issued from deep semi-circular pockets, or "glacial cirques," in the north flank of Alta Peak—the cirques in which lie Heather Lake, Emerald Lake, and Pear Lake. Other small branch glaciers came down the flanks of Mount Silliman, on the north side, and all united to form one mighty trunk glacier which plunged into Tokopah Valley, doubtless forming magnificent ice cascades. It moved probably at a rate of only a foot or two per day, but its motion was rapid enough to cause the relatively brittle ice in the upper layers to break and become rent by innumerable intersecting fissures or "crevasses."

As the snow continued to accumulate, owing to the severity of the climate, the Tokopah Glacier, as it may be called, grew thicker and longer, until at last it reached a point in the canyon about three miles below the site of the present highway bridge. Its total length, measured from the top of the Tableland to its terminus was therefore about nine miles. It was one of the smaller glaciers of the Sierra Nevada, but nonetheless an extremely interesting one.

How can the former extent of such a glacier be determined, it may be asked? The glacier polish and scratches might suggest themselves as good evidence, but unfortunately they are not permanent enough, for the rock scales off as it weathers. A more reliable method is by tracing the boulder ridges that accumulated along the margins of the glacier and at its front. The blocks and slabs which the glacier plucked and quarried out in its upper course were deposited as it melted in its lower course, and so it built up marginal ridges or "moraines," as they are termed by geologists, following the Swiss usage. These boulder ridges are enduring features and remain in existence for thousands of years after the glacier has vanished, outlining faithfully its precise shape and extent. Well preserved, continuous moraines are to be seen on both sides of the valley in which Lodgepole Camp is situated. Particularly prominent are those on the south side.

Alta Peak, Mount Silliman, Pear Lake and the Tableland.
Courtesy George Mauger, Sequoia and Kings Canyon National Parks Company

The trail to Heather Lake, which starts at the upper Wolverton Creek bridge, follows the crest of the highest moraine for part of the way, and where the crest is too bouldery, follows the outer or south slope of the moraine. In some places it follows the trough between two parallel moraines. Anyone who walks along this trail observantly will readily see that the glacier built two and in places three parallel moraines. They record periods of maximum ice volume each of which doubtless lasted a century or more and was separated from the preceding by an interval when the glacier, because of a short period of milder climate, had melted down somewhat.

From the crest of the highest moraine one looks down more than 100 feet upon Wolverton Creek, which for a distance of nearly two miles runs along the base of the embankment. Wolverton Creek, which heads in Panther Gap, runs northwestward throughout its upper course (which has remained unglaciated)—that is, it runs directly toward Lodgepole. Doubtless it continued northwestward all the way before the glacier came, but when the latter built its massive morainal embankments, the stream was deflected and forced to run southwestward for two miles. Then it found a weak place in the moraine and broke through.

Slopes of Alta Peak, winter. By David Brower

On the north side of Lodgepole, Silliman Creek likewise breaks through the morainal embankment, but that stream is not deflected. The reason is, no doubt, that its upper valley formerly contained a glacier (which headed in two cirques on Mount Silliman), and when that glacier was actively melting, the stream had many times its present volume and correspondingly great eroding power. It is entirely probable that when the Tokopah Glacier finally subsided, Silliman Creek broke through the morainal embankment rather suddenly, for its trench is flanked on each side by a ridge of boulders, and such "boulder levees," it is well known from observation on torrent channels, can be thrown up only by a tremendous rush of waters.

The top of the highest moraine on the south side of Lodgepole Valley indicates the highest level to which the ancient glacier's surface rose. It is about 1300 feet above the floor of the valley at the lower end of Tokopah, and accordingly it is clear that the ice there actually had a depth or thickness of 1300 feet. Downvalleyward the depth of ice diminished by degrees until it was only about a hundred feet at the terminus. On both sides of the valley the moraines can readily be traced down to the highway, which cuts through them, revealing the boulders, cobbles, and sand of which they are made up. The best example is just below the Wolverton Creek bridge on the highway.

Below the highway the moraines are very fragmentary and finally are reduced to a few scattered boulders, the reason being that the rocky sides of the gorge are too steep to give lodgement to loose material. Most of the glacial boulders there have rolled down, and the sand has been washed away. As a consequence the precise spot at which the Tokopah Glacier ended can not be located definitely.

As the Ice Age drew to a close the glacier melted back toward its sources, but it made occasional feeble readvances as a result of climatic oscillations. Some of these readvances are attested by small moraines that extend from the sides of the valley partway across the floor. A particularly fine example of such a "recessional moraine" is to be seen a short distance above the campfire place. Another, somewhat less distinct recessional moraine is situated just above the highway bridge. Each of these moraines originally extended across the entire width of the valley in the form of a loop outlining the end of the glacier, but all of them have been cut through and in part demolished by the river.

During its further recession the Tokopah Glacier liberated enormous quantities of boulders, cobbles, and sand, and these were washed out from its front by the river and deposited in the deeper parts of the valley, and so it is that the latter is filled with "glacial outwash material" for considerable distances. Most of the campsites are on the fairly even, yet bouldery surface of this filling, which varies in thickness from a few feet to as much as 30 feet in some places. Since glacial times the river, being no longer overloaded, has trenched the filling, and it is at the present time still cutting the loose material away little by little.

The Ice Age, as a matter of fact, consisted not of a single longdrawn period of glacial conditions but of several distinct glacial epochs or "stages" that were separated from one another by lengthy "interglacial stages" when the climate was fully as warm as it is today and when the glaciers melted far back toward their sources or vanished entirely. The moraines just described are merely those of the last glacial stage, which ended 20,000 years ago. They are most readily recognized because freshest. But if one looks more closely one can also discern moraines of the next earlier stage. They are poorly preserved, have lost their sharp crests, and are now composed largely of badly weathered, partly decomposed boulders. Their age is probably at least 250,000 years. The best places to see these are in the road cuts along the highway. After one has passed Wolverton Creek (going towards Giant Forest) one can see yellowish boulders and cobbles embedded in granite sand for a distance of nearly half a mile. Similarly when driving toward the General Grant Grove, after one has passed the outermost moraine of the last glacial stage, half way between Silliman Creek and Clover Creek, one continues to see the yellowish, rotten boulders of the earlier glacial stage for another mile or more—far beyond Clover Creek bridge.

The Tokopah Glacier of the earlier ice stage reached much farther down the canyon of the Marble Fork than its successor of the last ice stage. The exact spot where it ended can not be determined for lack of morainal material on the steep sides of the canyon, but to judge from the positions of the older moraines as far as they can be traced, the glacier in all probability reached no farther than the mouth of Halstedt Creek. Since the glacier melted away, the canyon has been deepened considerably by the river, and so all traces of the earlier glaciation have been destroyed.

An essay written by Dr. Matthes, probably in the middle or late '30's, in connection with the interpretative program of Sequoia National Park. So far as known, it was not printed, but used only in typewritten form.

AVALANCHE SCULPTURE

IN THE SIERRA NEVADA

AVALANCHES of snow, their mode and frequency of occurrence in mountains of high relief, the menace they constitute to life and property, and their eroding action on cliffs and mountain slopes, have long been subjects of scientific study in certain parts of Europe; but in the United States, whose lofty western ranges are but sparsely inhabited, and where the economic need for their study has thus far been relatively slight, avalanches have received until recently hardly any attention from either geographers or geologists. During the summers of 1935 and 1936, however, the author, while engaged in geomorphologic and glaciologic studies in the Sierra Nevada of California, became aware of the important part which avalanches there play, and have played throughout probably all of Pleistocene time, as eroding agents, more especially in the region above the timber line—the alpine zone—where they produce a distinctive type of cliff sculpture. On and in the vicinity of Mount Whitney, the culminating peak of the range, and the highest in the continental United States, that type of cliff sculpture attains an exceptional degree of perfection and regularity, and accordingly he feels impelled to offer this brief note as a firstling contribution from the United States to the study of avalanche action.

Perhaps it will duplicate in some measure the excellent work of European observers, notably that of Allix,[1] but he feels justified nevertheless in presenting the results of his own studies, because they were made in a mountain district where topography, rock structure and climatic conditions together have permitted the three erosional processes characteristic of the alpine zone—glacial

---

[1] The author freely confesses that he was not acquainted with the results of Allix's studies when he made his own observations in the Sierra Nevada. His attention was invited to Allix's work only recently, but, being out in the field and unable to visit a library, he has had to proceed with the writing of this note—in camp—without having had opportunity to familiarize himself with Allix's observations and conclusions.

action, avalanche action and nivation—to produce their respective type forms with great distinctness, and where because of slow rock weathering those forms remain exceptionally well preserved.

In order that the reasons for this singularly fine development of type forms may be understood it should be explained, first, that the mountains in question are, in spite of their great altitude—which ranges from 12,000 to over 14,000 feet—prevailingly full-bodied, having escaped complete dissection during the cycle of stream erosion which preceded glaciation. Many of them possess, in consequence, gently sloping summit platforms of considerable extent that are undivided by streamcut gulches but sharply bounded by the headwalls of glacial cirques hewn in the sides of the mountains. These summit platforms, although surrounded by the very sources of the Pleistocene glaciers, have themselves remained unglaciated, being windswept throughout. The snow that fell upon them in glacial times was, as it is now, in large part blown away by the fierce gales of winter, and was never permitted to accumulate to sufficient depth to form gravitating glaciers. It lay only in stationary drifts and fields of moderate thickness, promoting with its melt-water the process of nivation.

The summit platforms of Mount Whitney and of the other tabular peaks in its vicinity are therefore typical nivated areas, where the rock has been riven into fragments, and is still being riven, by recurrent freezings and thawings, but where no effective transporting agent in the form of stream or glacier was available during glacial times, nor is at present, to remove the frost-split fragments.

The cirques and canyons below, again, appear never to have been filled with glacial ice to their full capacity, as were the cirques and canyons farther north in the Sierra Nevada. The great majority of them were filled only to approximately one-half their depth, some of them even to less than one-half. This fact is shown clearly on their walls by the height of the upper limit of glaciation, which, as may be seen in the photographic illustrations, is almost everywhere conspicuous and unmistakable, because of the contrast between the angular sculpture of the cliffs above it and the smooth forms of the glaciated rock surfaces below; also because the canyon walls have suffered on the whole but little from postglacial weathering. The maximum depth which the glaciers of the Wisconsin (Würm) stage[2] attained in the cirques and canyons of the Mount

[2] Referred to in other essays as the later glacial stage, in distinction from the earlier of the two well-recorded stages (the El Portal) in this part of the Sierra Nevada. "Würm" is the European equivalent.—ED.

Whitney district can therefore be definitely determined as having ranged between 500 and 1200 feet. As a rule it was less than 1000 feet,[3] and as a consequence the rock walls rose from 500 to 1500 feet above the glaciers.

It is on these unglaciated rock walls, at the heads of the cirques as well as on the sides of the canyons, that the evidences of avalanche erosion are best displayed. These rock walls owe their steep profiles primarily to the undercutting

The gently sloping tabular summits of the Mount Whitney district are nivated but not glaciated. Their walls above the limit of glaciation are deeply fluted by alternating snow chutes and rock ribs. By François Matthes

action of the glaciers, which enlarged the cirques and widened the canyons at the expense of the intermediate divides. Three dismantling processes, however, have tended to maintain their profiles at angles of less than 90° to the horizontal —the freezing of water in joints and other fractures, resulting in the loosening of blocks and slabs of rock; the pull of gravity on these loosened fragments and all rock masses in unstable equilibrium; and the eroding action of recurring avalanches of snow carrying abrading rock fragments with them.

[3] These relatively shallow glaciers, it should be explained, were nevertheless many miles in length and were tributary to the great Kern Glacier, which filled the Kern Canyon to depths of 2500 feet and more, and attained a length of 26 miles.

The last named process deserves, in the author's opinion, more recognition than it has been generally accorded thus far; for his observations have shown him that the distinctive type of cliff sculpture which it produces occurs in a large percentage of the glacial cirques and canyons, not only in the Mount Whitney district but elsewhere in the Sierra Nevada, and likewise in certain parts of the Rocky Mountains and the Cascade Range. It occurs, in fact, wher-

Typical snow chutes on the north face of Mount Hitchcock. The snow chutes are carved to depths of 50 to 100 feet in disregard of the joint structure of the granite. All terminate at the upper limit of glaciation which is clearly marked. Below is the glaciated floor of Whitney Canyon. By François Matthes

ever the rock structure does not interfere with the orderly development of the forms.

Avalanche sculpture, wherever it is well developed, gives the cliffs a distinctly fluted appearance, there being an alternation of smoothly concave gullies and sharp rock ribs, all trending downward roughly parallel to one another in the direction of greatest declivity. That the smooth gullies are actually the pathways of recurring avalanches is known from direct observation and, besides, it is evident from the fact that a large pile of snow usually lies beneath each of them in the spring or early summer. In addition there is on the slope below each gully a cone of rock fragments carried down by the rushing snow masses.

Allix has referred to the alternating gullies and rock ribs, appropriately, as "cannelures."[4] That word, however, cannot well be taken over into the English vocabulary, and accordingly it seems desirable to find a suitable English word to denote the features in question. The word gully, used above in a preliminary way, is decidedly inappropriate, being associated in the minds of geographers and geologists with the action of running water. It is therefore proposed to employ

Postglacial weathering and avalanche sculpture along zones of shearing.
East face of Mount Hitchcock. By François Matthes

the term "chute," which implies a smoothly concave form through which masses of incoherent material can rush down with a minimum of friction. And inasmuch as it is desirable to link the forms with the material that passes through them and is instrumental in producing them, it seems appropriate to call them "snow chutes" and perhaps "avalanche chutes"—although the latter term is rather cumbersome and difficult to pronounce.

Snow chutes, as they will here be called, are not necessarily the equivalent of "chimneys" and "couloirs" of which alpinists make use in scaling peaks. Those

[4] Allix, André, "La morphologie glaciaire en Vercors," *Recueil des Travaux de L'Institut de Géographie Alpine de l'Université de Grenoble,* Vol. II, 1914, pp. 109–110.

narrow recesses in the flanks of mountains are produced primarily by differential weathering along vertical or nearly vertical zones of faulting or sheeted structures in the rock. The positions of many snow chutes, it is true, are determined by such structures, but it is equally true that many snow chutes occur in places where no lines or zones of weakness exist in the rock. On the cliffs of granitic rocks in the Sierra Nevada they were observed to cross the jointing at various angles. The most perfect forms were found in massive granite, wholly devoid of joint fractures. Such forms, produced solely by abrasion, are extremely smooth, with semi-circular or parabolic cross sections. To the mountaineer they offer no convenient routes for an ascent; on the contrary they are to be avoided by him, being too smooth and too slippery. Even in horizontally stratified rocks of sedimetary origin very smooth and regular chutes are often worn by avalanches. Excellent examples of this kind were observed by the author in Glacier National Park, Montana.

How entirely regardless of structure snow chutes may develop in some cliffs is well exemplified by the photograph on page 158. It shows a remarkably regular series of chutes worn in the north side of Mount Hitchcock (Sequoia National Park, California), which is composed of vertically sheeted granite, the strike of the fractures being from east to west—that is, at right angles to the direction of the chutes. The latter are, by estimation, fully 50 feet deep. A trickle of water is seen descending through one of the chutes. It appears as a dark line that might readily be mistaken for a little stream-cut trench. There is, however, no such trench. The water merely finds its way down over the smooth, concave bottom of the chute; it is in no wise instrumental in deepening the chute.

Inspection of the photograph shows that many of the chutes are wider at the top than at the bottom, and that not a few branch upward into two or more minor chutes, separated by small, attentuated rock ribs. The reason appears to be that the bulk of the windblown snow accumulates at the top of the cliff in the form of a massive cornice, and it is the sudden breaking and slipping down of sections of this cornice that initiates the avalanches. As the latter progress downward, more and more of their volume is dissipated into whirling spray, and as a consequence the lower parts of the chutes receive less wear than the upper parts and remain relatively narrow. Not infrequently, moreover, an avalanche, after rushing down through the upper half of a chute, comes to rest in the lower half, owing to the retarding action of snow that clogs its path.

Gigantic snow chute carved in massive granite, near Bearpaw Camp,
Sequoia National Park. By François Matthes

It deserves to be pointed out, finally, that the snow chutes on a given canyon wall all terminate at approximately the same height above the canyon floor— namely at the upper limit of glaciation. This is illustrated on page 158, but it can be observed in scores of glacial cirques and canyons throughout the Sierra Nevada. It demonstrates clearly that the chutes were formed largely, almost wholly, during glacial times, when the canyons were about one-half filled with ice. Avalanche action has of course continued since the disappearance of the glaciers and is frequent every winter at the present time; but the amount of erosional work that avalanches have accomplished in the resistant granitic rocks of the Sierra Nevada during postglacial time is decidedly small and in places almost negligible. As may be seen on page 158 cones of rock fragments beneath the chutes on Mount Hitchcock, which give a measure of postglacial avalanche erosion, are of small or at best, moderate volume; they contain but a small fraction of the total amount of material that has been carved out of the chutes. It is evident, moreover, that the chutes themselves have been prolonged downward but little below the upper limit of glaciation.

In mountain regions where the rocks weather more rapidly than in the Sierra Nevada, and where the canyon walls are dismantled at a correspondingly rapid rate, avalanche sculpture soon loses its characteristic forms and is likely to escape detection. Moreover, wherever the rock structure is highly irregular or the cliff sculpture is controlled by rock masses that vary greatly in resistance, the chances for the development of typical snow chutes are relatively small, and such forms may never become distinct. Such is the case in many parts of the Rocky Mountains, of the Cascade Range and of the great ranges of Alaska. Such is the case also in many parts of the European Alps; and so it is, doubtless, that avalanche sculpture has not been clearly recognized thus far, save in a few favorable localities, and has not yet taken its place along with the type forms of glaciation and nivation as a characteristic part of alpine morphology.

Reprinted from "Transactions of the Meetings of the International Commissions of Snow and of Glaciers," Edinburgh, September 1936. International Association of Hydrology, Bulletin 23, pages 631– 637. Riga, 1938.

r with the Swiss Alps I recently showed an
y. "What!" he exclaimed, in evident disap-
unt Whitney flat and featureless? I had
towering rock monument with sharp, sky-
eply, "Mount Whitney's summit is merely
hich, I suppose, holds little appeal for an
to a geologist specializing in the study of
pture that summit platform is a feature of
eptional interest. I grant you that in point of
cannot compare with the dazzling Jungfrau
t, to one who can read it, the story told by
t and goes back to much more remote ages
glamorous alpine peaks. Indeed, the more
of repeated visits to and flights around and
erable, the more precious seems that bit of
it I have never set foot without a certain

plain.
region of great altitude that is profoundly
and valleys, sharp crests and pointed peaks
s of the canyons and valleys lead more or
and summits, and there meet one another
n so dissected has been intensely glaciated,
is likely to be still more pronounced; for
canyons they occupy, and this widening is
iate divides. The widening process, more-

over, is carried all the way to the extreme canyon-heads, and as a result these are enlarged from V-shaped gulches and ravines to broadly U-shaped amphitheaters, or cirques. Biting into the mountains from opposite sides these cirques transform the crests and spurs between them to attenuated comb-ridges or cleavers, and sharpen the peaks to three- or four-edged pyramids with concave sides. These types of mountain sculpture are familiar to all who have climbed in the Alps, or for that matter, in other strongly glaciated alpine regions. They are characteristic also of the High Sierra, and predominate in any extended view of it.

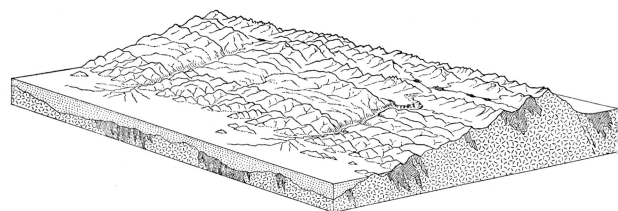

Figure 12.—Idealized representation of a portion of the tilted Sierra block, showing the "roots" of the ancestral Sierras penetrating deep into the granite; also longitudinal crests and valleys. Vertical scale exaggerated

Mount Whitney's gently sloping tabular summit, it will be readily seen, belongs to an entirely different category. It is manifestly not an alpine mountain form. It could not possibly have been fashioned at its present high level by the erosional processes described. On the contrary, it is being destroyed by them; for, as the surrounding precipices continue to crumble and spall off, the platform will grow smaller and smaller until at last it will cease to exist. Evidently, it is a much older feature than any of the sharply sculptured alpine peaks around it; it is a remnant of an ancient landscape, the rest of which already has been carried away. What manner of landscape was this? How was it formed, and how long ago?

Be it understood, at the outset, that the Sierra Nevada, which is a huge tilted block of the earth's crust, slanting toward the west, is not the first mountain range to occupy the region east of the Great Valley of California. Long before it was uplifted, another mountain range, or to be more accurate, a system of mountain ranges, stood in the same place. And that earlier mountain system, itself, was a late comer in geologic history; for it arose in the Mesozoic era, the era of giant reptiles, only about one hundred million years ago, after the earth had been troubled with spasmodic heavings and sinkings for upward of one and a half billion years.[1] A complete record of all those successive disturbances probably will never be obtained, for the evidences grow more and more fragmentary, the farther back they are pursued; but this much is definitely known, that during those vast stretches of time the area now occupied by the Sierra Nevada was alternatingly ocean-bottom and land, and when it was land it bore, as a rule, hills and even mountains of some height.

With those remote and as yet vaguely known events we need not further concern ourselves in this study of Mount Whitney—though merely to be aware of their occurrence gives us a tremendous perspective of earth history. It is with the mountain system that preceded the advent of the present Sierra Nevada that we must begin. What has become of it? Are any of its mountains and valleys still in existence? No, they have been completely annihilated, eradicated from the face of the earth; but fortunately some of the roots, if we may call them such, remain incorporated in the body of the present Sierra, and from these it is possible with some confidence to infer the structure and even the topography of those ancestral Sierras. They were carved evidently from great wavelike folds or wrinkles in the earth's crust produced by the buckling of originally flat lying strata, and they must have had the aspect of roughly parallel mountain ridges similar to those of the Appalachian system but trending in general from northwest to southeast. These ancestral Sierras were in existence for nearly 80 million years and in that time were gradually worn down by the processes of erosion until nothing remained, presumably, but rows of hills in a lowland that sloped gently down to the sea. Between those hills, which were composed of the more obdurate rocks, the streams followed belts of less resistant rocks, mostly in northwesterly or southeasterly directions.

Then, about 50 to 60 million years ago, shortly after the dawn of the Cenozoic era—the era of mammals and the latest great time divisions of geologic history—began the first uplifts that led to the rise of the present range. They tilted the Sierra region and the country to the east of it toward the southwest, and as a result a new system of southwestward flowing master streams came into

[1] See footnote on page 97, and Appendix.—ED.

existence; but many of the lesser streams between the ridges, unable to shift, maintained their southeasterly or northwesterly courses. Trenching deeper with every succeeding uplift, they eventually cut through the lowest of the folded strata and graved their valleys in the granite underneath—the granite which had welled up in a molten state from the depths of the earth and had crystallized under the folds of the ancestral Sierras. And so the northwest-southeast trend of those ancient mountains was perpetuated in the landscape of the present range.

Little attention—altogether too little—has been paid to the significance of the crests and valleys of the Sierra Nevada that trend in northwesterly or south-easterly directions, roughly parallel to the main crest-line and at right angles to the master canyons, which drain more or less directly down the western slope. These multiple crests, with their jagged peaks, have led us to speak, familiarly, of "the Sierras" and justify the use of the plural form. They are now seen to be the very oldest features in the landscape of the range, an inheritance from the long departed ancestral Sierras.

Some of the longitudinal crests of the Sierra Nevada are still composed of folded strata left from the earlier mountain system, but many of them are carved wholly out of granite. A striking example of the former kind is the Ritter Range, which is made largely of ancient folded volcanic rocks. The southeastward trending upper canyon of the Middle Fork of the San Joaquin, which parallels the Ritter Range as far south as the head of Pumice Flat, is cut in other volcanic rocks of the same relict mass, and closely follows the direction or "strike" of the

Aerial view of Mount Whitney and the Upper Kern Basin, with Table Mountain in the distance. By Roy Curtis, Reno, Nevada

upturned beds. On the other hand, the Clark Range and the Cathedral Range, in Yosemite National Park, are made entirely of granite, save for a few small patches of stratified rocks; and the upper Merced Canyon and Lyell Canyon are cut in granite throughout. The Le Conte Divide, again, is carved out of an isolated mass of stratified rocks, and Goddard Canyon is excavated in the same dark-hued materials. Both trend with the northwesterly strike of the beds. By contrast, the Kaiser Crest, above Huntington Lake, and its southeastward extension, the Kaiser Ridge, together form a continuous rampart of granite 25 miles in length. (Only one small strip of marble remains near the Twin Lakes, north of the Kaiser Crest.) And the South Fork of the San Joaquin has cut its northwestward trending canyon in granite all the way from the head of Blaney Meadow to its junction with the Middle Fork.

Farther south, in the headwaters of the Kings River and in Sequoia National Park, where the folded structures of the ancestral Sierras bend gradually south-southeastward, the principal lineaments of the High Sierra notably bend in the same direction, although they are carved for the greater part out of granite. There, to mention only those most directly related to our theme, are the Great Western Divide, which contains stratified rocks in the vicinity of Mineral King and in the Kaweah Group; the upper Kern Canyon, which is cut entirely in granite, along a nearly straight north-south fault; and, to the east of it, the culminating crest of the Sierra Nevada, which bears Mount Whitney and is composed of granite throughout.

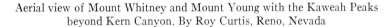

Aerial view of Mount Whitney and Mount Young with the Kaweah Peaks
beyond Kern Canyon. By Roy Curtis, Reno, Nevada

The crest last mentioned deserves closer scrutiny. A distinct mountain range it is, stretching in a south-southeasterly direction for a distance of 17 miles—from the Shepherd Pass on the north, to the Cottonwood Pass on the south. Surmounted by seven of the eleven 14,000-foot peaks of the Sierra Nevada —Tyndall, Williamson, Barnard, Russell, Whitney, Muir, and Langley—and

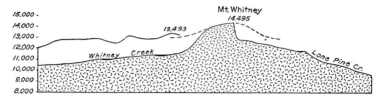

Figure 13.—East-west profile of Mount Whitney. The broken line indicates the approximate outlines of ancient "Whitney Hill." Vertical scale same as horizontal scale

by several peaks only a few tens of feet below the 14,000-foot level, it is the most lofty of all the longitudinal crests of the range. Curiously, it is still unnamed, although it certainly deserves and needs a name much more than some of the subordinate crests that are well provided for in this respect. In the following pages the immediate need of a suitable name for that distinct and culminating topographic unit of the Sierra Nevada will be manifest, and accordingly a name is proposed for it here and now—*Muir Crest*.[2] Though not yet formally submitted for approval, that name will here be used, at least provisionally.

That the Muir Crest, like the other longitudinal crests cited, has inherited its southeasterly trend from the ancestral Sierras, seems hardly open to doubt, for there is nothing in the joint-structure of its granitic rocks that could have determined that trend. The Kern Canyon, to the west of it, differs it is true, from the rank and file of longitudinal valleys in the Sierra Nevada in that its course is determined by a fault, a long fracture in the Sierra block, but, to judge from the older features of its landscape and from its great breadth, the upper Kern Basin as a whole has been developed from a very ancient valley and is essentially analogous to Center Basin and the canyons of East Creek and Sphinx Creek, to the north, and Cloud Canyon, to the northwest. It probably antedates the fault, though it is possible that the fault, too, is of great antiquity.

[2] The small peak that bears Muir's name at present seems hardly commensurate in importance among the features of the Sierra Nevada with the greatness of the man whose love for the "Range of Light" inspired the movement for the conservation of its scenic treasures.

A number of features on the east flank of the Muir Crest, furthermore, point unmistakably to the former existence, several miles farther to eastward, of another longitudinal valley of great antiquity, a valley that long antedated the down-faulting of Owens Valley and the formation of the imposing east front of the Sierra Nevada. Most definite is the evidence presented by the eastern spur of Mount Le Conte which terminates in Lone Pine Peak, and by similar spurs east of Mount Langley. There is, therefore, ample warrant for the belief that the Muir Crest was developed, by valley-deepening to the west and the east of it, from a row of lowland hills, relics of the destroyed ancestral Sierras.

Is it then to be inferred, you may ask, that the summit platform of Mount Whitney is a remnant of one of those ancient lowland hills? A daring thought, it seems, yet that is precisely what its configuration appears to indicate. Indeed, that summit platform has, so far as it is preserved, all the characteristics of a lowland hill. Its gentle westward slope could not possibly have been fashioned

Aerial view of Mount Whitney (from the north), Mount Russell, Mount Hitchcock, and Mount Langley. By Francis P. Farquhar

by ordinary erosive processes at its present high level, 3000 feet above steep-walled Whitney Canyon, but must have been graded with reference to a relatively shallow vale or valley at its western base. The depth of that ancient valley can be determined, at least approximately, by plotting, true to scale, the east-west profile of Mount Whitney's summit from the contour lines of the topographic map, and then extending that profile westward to the axis of Whitney Canyon in a curve such as might be expected in a landscape of subdued hills. The profile plot, shown in Figure 13, indicates a depth for the ancient valley of about 1500 feet. This figure can of course lay no claim to accuracy, for the contouring of Mount Whitney's summit on the small-scale map is necessarily generalized, but the curve is drawn in accordance with the principles of geomorphology, the science of land forms, and at least affords us a rough measure of the height of ancient "Whitney Hill." The altitude of "Whitney Hill" above sea level naturally was much more than 1500 feet, for the hill was situated fully 50 miles in air line —more than 100 miles by the roundabout course of the Kern River—from the seaboard, which then lay not far from the foothills of the present range. From analogy with other lowlands produced by long-continued erosion, it may be estimated that the valley at the west base of "Whitney Hill" had an elevation of about 500 feet. Whitney Hill itself therefore rose probably as much as 2000 feet above the sea.

The landscape of the High Sierra affords many bits of supporting evidence for this interpretation of Mount Whitney's origin. In the first place, Mount Langley's summit, which is but a few hundred feet lower than Mount Whitney's, is of the same gently sloping tabular type. Its summit profile, when carefully plotted like that of Mount Whitney, and then extended westward to the axis of Rock Creek Canyon, indicates for the original "Langley Hill" a height closely comparable to that of "Whitney Hill."

Again, the Great Western Divide and its long north-northwestward and south-southeastward trending spurs, which must have originated in much the same way as the Muir Crest, bear several peaks with flat or gently sloping tabular summits. Most noteworthy is Table Mountain (13,646), but hardly less typical, though less clean cut, is the tabular peak (13,300) between Milestone Mountain and the Colby Pass, which might well be called Milestone Mesa. And on the Kern Ridge nearby are two more unnamed mountains with gently sloping summit platforms, 13,560 and 13,206 feet high, respectively. These tabular summits ranging within a few hundred feet of one another in altitude, clearly represent remnants of a group of ancient hills. The fact that they average about 1000 feet lower in altitude than the comparable summits on the Muir Crest does not argue against the probability of their having been derived from the same ancient landscape as the latter, for the Great Western Divide stands 10 to 15 miles west of the Muir Crest and consequently about a thousand feet lower on the westward sloping body of the Sierra Nevada.

Aerial view of the Muir Crest, Lone Pine and the Alabama Hills in the foreground.
By Roy Curtis, Reno, Nevada

Farther north in the range still other tabular peaks dominate its sky line. Notable examples are Mount Darwin, which has two detached summit platforms, 13,841 and 13,701 feet in altitude, respectively; and Kuna, Koip, and Blacktop peaks, in Yosemite National Park, which together form a continuous platform 3½ miles long and ranging between 12,500 and 13,000 feet in altitude. Parker Peak (12,850), Mount Gibbs (12,700), and Mount Dana (13,050) bear remnants of the same ancient undulating landscape. The acuminate peak of Mount Dana is the most prominent hill of all, but even it rises only 700 feet above the platform at its east base. To those who have firsthand acquaintance with these crests it is readily evident that their tabular summits, which decline steadily northward with the entire body of the range, represent isolated remnants of a once continuous landscape of moderate relief, an ancient lowland now raised to great height on the present range.

It is now in order to relate briefly how by successive steps lofty Mount Whitney has evolved from lowly "Whitney Hill." This story, of course, has to do primarily with the successive uptiltings of the Sierra Nevada and the cycles of erosion that were initiated by them. But where, you will probably ask, is the record of those uplifts to be found? In the features of the landscape itself. Professor Lawson was the first to spell out the principal chapters of that history from an analysis of the landscape of the upper Kern Basin, and that classic analysis will here be followed, though with certain modifications and additions indicated by the more complete knowledge now at hand.[3]

Be it observed, in the first place, that Mount Whitney outtops by fully one thousand feet all the other mountains in its immediate neighborhood that have rounded or gently sloping summits—notably Mount Young[4] (13,493) and Mount Hitchcock (13,188). The disparity in height is manifest in the aerial view looking northwestward over Mount Whitney and Mount Young. It is likewise patent from the profile plot in Figure 13, which shows that the summit of Mount Young originally rose but a few hundred feet above the vale at the west base of "Whitney Hill." Mount Langley similarly outtops the rounded summit (13,481) of the unnamed massif to the west of Rock Creek Canyon, as well as Lone Pine Peak (12,951), to the northeast, and Cirque Peak (12,863), to the south. The smoothly curving slopes of these lesser mountains, moreover, descend to levels close to 12,000 feet, and appear to have been fashioned with reference to much lower valley-floors than the summit platforms of either Mount Whitney or Mount Langley. It is to be inferred, therefore, that the intial uplift of the region caused the streams to intrench themselves a thousand feet or more on both sides of the Muir Crest. During the ensuing stillstand of the earth's crust their valleys widened gradually and the mountain slopes were worn back to moderate angles. Mount Whitney, as a result of this first uplift, probably gained some two thousand feet in altitude above the sea, and, because of the valley-cutting, came

---

[3] "The Geomorphogeny of the Upper Kern Basin," by Andrew C. Lawson, in *University of California Publications, Bulletin of the Department of Geology*, 1904, 3:15, pp. 305–330.

[4] Since this essay was originally written, the higher part of Mount Young has been given the name Mount Hale.—ED.

to stand 500 or 600 feet higher above its immediate base. Moreover, long spurs were carved on both sides of the Muir Crest, spurs such as are now represented by Mount Young and Lone Pine Peak.

To the west of Cirque Peak, and about 1500 feet below the level of its rounded summit, is an undulating plateau that stretches unbroken for a distance of seven miles toward the Kern Canyon. The principal valley on that plateau, broad and level, goes by the name of Siberian Outpost. For the summit tract, which is of far greater extent than the valley, and even more frigid and more windswept, the name Boreal Plateau has recently been proposed. This plateau unquestionably represents a large remnant of an erosion surface of moderate relief that was formed throughout the upper Kern Basin during a prolonged period of erosion following a second great uplift. Other remnants of this ancient erosion surface are Guyot Flat, to the northwest of Mount Guyot, and the Bighorn Plateau, between Wallace Creek and Tyndall Creek. The valley profiles for this stage of development of the upper Kern Basin are not all drawn at the time of this writing, and consequently only rough estimates can here be given for the magnitude of the second uplift and the consequent further gain in height of Mount Whitney. The peak was raised presumably about 3000 feet higher, and therefore attained an altitude of, roughly, 7000 feet above the sea. As a result of further valley cutting by Whitney Creek its height above its west base was increased probably to somewhat more than 2000 feet.

About 1500 feet below the general level of the Boreal Plateau, again, lie the broad, gently sloping rock-benches that flank the Kern Canyon proper. Representative of these is the Chagoopa Plateau, which rises from an elevation of 8600 feet at the canyon rim to about 10,500 feet at the base of the mountains. Those benches clearly are remnants of a former floor of the Kern Basin that was developed to great breadth during an erosion cycle following a third uplift. The magnitude of that uplift also can, for the present, only be estimated roughly. It amounted probably to some 2000 feet, and therefore raised the summit of Mount Whitney to an altitude of about 9000 feet.

The Kern Canyon itself was, of course, trenched in consequence of the last great uplift. That uplift took place, to judge from the best data now available, about the beginning of the Ice Age, and the canyon is therefore really a product of alternating stream and glacial erosion. Like the Yosemite, its upper portion was three times invaded and remodeled by a mighty trunk glacier, and to the repeated glacial remodeling it owes its pronounced U-shape. The depth of the

Table Mountain on the Great Western Divide, with its gently sloping tabular summit, represents the same ancient landscape surface as Mount Whitney and other summits on the Muir Crest. ten miles to the east. Milestone Mountain in the middle distance with the Red Spur on the skyline.

canyon below the flanking benches of the Chagoopa cycle—2000 to 2500 feet— affords, nevertheless, no index of the magnitude of the uplift, for that event occurred but a short time ago, in the geologic sense, and the river has not yet had sufficient time to trench deeply. The cycle of erosion started by the uplift is still in full swing today, and the river doubtless will continue to trench for a long time to come. From studies made in the Yosemite region, meanwhile, it is evident that the last uplift of the Sierra Nevada far exceeded all previous uplifts in magnitude, adding about 6000 feet to the height of the central part of the range. It may be presumed, therefore, that the Muir Crest was also raised at least 6000 feet, and that Mount Whitney thereby gained substantially its present altitude.

The recency of the last uplift accounts also for the slight headway which Whitney Creek has made in cutting its valley down to the level of the main

Trail to Mount Whitney. By Cedric Wright

canyon. Like Wallace Creek and Rock Creek, it has cut a gulch only one mile long, and through that gulch it tumbles precipitously from a gently sloping untrenched upland valley, a "hanging valley" comparable to those of the Yosemite region. It follows that that upland valley has not yet felt the effects of the last cycle of erosion and still is a part of the landscape of the Chagoopa cycle, modified, of course by glacial action.

The extent to which the upland valley of Whitney Creek has been remodeled by glacial action varies considerably in its different parts. In its lower portion where the ice never exceeded 600 feet in depth—as is shown by the lateral moraines—the valley suffered but moderate changes, but at the immediate base of Mount Whitney, where the two branches of the "Whitney Glacier" coalesced, a radical transformation was effected. The ice there attained a depth of over 1000 feet, and because of this greater depth and the longer duration of its action, it was able to add several hundred feet to the depth of the canyon and even more to its breadth. There can be no doubt that the present broad U-shape of

Whitney Canyon was evolved by glaciation from a relatively narrow preglacial V-shape, but so thoroughgoing has been the transformation that it is difficult from the present topography to judge what the preglacial features may have looked like.

During the first half of the Ice Age there also took place the tremendous dislocation of the earth's crust that resulted in the formation of the imposing eastern front of the Sierra Nevada. Opinions of geologists still differ as regards the precise nature of that dislocation, but it seems probable from the latest field data now at hand, that it consisted in the main of a sinking of Owens Valley between parallel faults at the bases of the Sierra Nevada and the Inyo Range; also, that this subsidence occurred after the Sierra Nevada had attained approximately its present height and had suffered its first glaciation. The dislocation probably was not instantaneous, but was effected by many successive jerky movements spaced at intervals over a period thousands of years in length.

While it was thus growing, the eastern front of the Sierra Nevada was constantly subject to erosion, the more intense because of its steepness, and so it became deeply gashed by canyons and gulches. The extent to which it has been dissected and worn back is at first difficult to evaluate. Standing on the extreme summit of Mount Whitney, at the brink of its great east-facing cliff, one is apt to gain the impression that the fault fracture is right at one's feet, yet it is manifest from the projecting spur that terminates in Lone Pine Peak, and from the long spurs to the east of Mount Langley, all of which bear remnants of ancient erosion surfaces, that the original fault escarpment must have stood at least four or five miles east of Mount Whitney's summit.

Stream erosion on the eastern front of the range was supplemented at least twice by glacial erosion, most vigorously at the heads of the canyons and gulches, less so toward their lower ends. Capacious cirques were developed on the northerly and easterly sides of the peaks, and as the curving cirque walls receded under the combined attacks of quarrying glaciers and rock-splitting frosts, they bit deeper and deeper into the body of the Muir Crest, destroying the old preglacial slopes and spurs, carrying away even the main divide, as in the stretch between Mount Whitney and the Whitney Pass, where only the western slope now remains. In some places, as to the south of Mount Le Conte, the divide, attacked from both sides, was transformed to a narrow, pinnacled comb-ridge; elsewhere, as between Mount Whitney and Mount Russell, it was reduced by the headward quarrying of opposing glaciers to a low, frail rock-partition, and in a few spots, as between Mount McAdie and Mount Mallory, the divide was demolished altogether and replaced by a smoothly concave saddle or col.

A very massive, full-bodied mountain preglacial Mount Whitney must have been, else it would have been reduced, like its smaller neighbor, Mount Russell, to an attenuated alpine crag. To judge from its present outlines, its entire eastern half has been cut away by cirque glaciers. Those glaciers were small but doubt-

Wasting blocks of aplite, summit of Mount Whitney. By François Matthes

less long-lived, by reason of their unusually favorable locations, and they probably carried on their destructive work not only during each glacial stage but also for long periods during each interglacial stage and throughout most of the postglacial interval. They have vanished only quite recently, and even today frost sapping at the base of Whitney's cliff is promoted by lingering snowdrifts.

From the north side of the mountain a broad slice was removed by the widening of the glacial canyon that lies between it and Mount Russell, and on the west side the lower preglacial slope was destroyed by the glacial widening of

Whitney Canyon. The southeast side lost a small slice as a result of the incision of a narrow cleft, the northernmost of the series of clefts that gash the crestline at intervals for more than a mile to the south of Mount Whitney. These clefts—the breathtaking "windows" that afford occasional peeps to the eastward from the trail—are not glacial features, but have been etched out, so to speak, by frost action seconded by snow avalanches along vertical zones in which the granite as

House on Mount Whitney and frost-heaved blocks of aplite. By François Matthes

a result of ancient faulting movements is sheared into thin, fragile plates. Only on its southwest side Mount Whitney still retains its preglacial slope approximately intact and there connects with the equally unglaciated western slope of the main divide.

One of the most astounding features of Mount Whitney is that, although situated in the center of a district from which glaciers formerly radiated in all directions, its own summit platform and the upper portions of its sides have remained unglaciated. Not the slightest evidence of glacial action, whether in the form of polish, striae, or moraines, is to be found on the summit platform; and as for the canyons at the immediate base of the mountain, these, it is clear from the moderate height to which their walls appear smoothed by lengthwise glacial corrasion, were never filled with ice to more than one-half of their depth. The effects of glacial corrasion which they exhibit are, of course, only those produced by the later glaciers, but it is manifest from the height and the gradients of the older moraines on the sides of Whitney Canyon that the earlier glaciers, there as in other parts of the Sierra Nevada, had no greater depth in the cirques and upper canyons than the later glaciers.

A similar dearth of glacial ice prevailed throughout the entire extent of the Muir Crest, as is shown by the low "ice lines" in all its canyons and by its numerous unglaciated summits and spurs. This state of things, which must have contrasted with the superabundance of glacial ice in the upper San Joaquin and upper Tuolumne basins, was due in part to the position of the Muir Crest close to the southern limit of glaciation in the Sierra Nevada, which coincides approximately with the southern limit of the High Sierra, properly speaking; and in part, also, to the fact that the Muir Crest was then, as now, robbed of its rightful share of snow by the Great Western Divide, upon which the snow clouds, driven up by southwesterly winds, unload the bulk of their white burden.

The sides of Mount Whitney, in so far as they rise above the level of the ancient glaciers, are furrowed by parallel or converging gullies, as much as 50 or even 100 feet in depth. Where these are spaced at close intervals, they are separated only by sharp, craggy rock-ribs, and the cliffs have a distinctly fluted appearance in consequence. These gullies, it is now realized, have been worn, not by streams of water, but by avalanchess of snow shod with rocks. They are, indeed, characteristic forms of avalanche sculpture that have not until recently been recognized as such in this country. The bottoms of these gullies are smoothly concave, as a result of the rasping action of frequent avalanches, and remind one of coal chutes such as are used for the unloading of coal cars or coal trucks by gravity. The term "snow chutes" (or perhaps "avalanche chutes") therefore seems appropriate for them.

Snow chutes are numerous on both the north and west sides of Mount Whitney, but those on the west side are developed on the grandest scale. Still more perfect, though perhaps less deep, are the snow chutes on the north side of Mount Hitchcock and in the cirque at the head of Whitney Canyon. The Mount Whitney district is, in fact, remarkably rich in avalanche sculpture, far richer than the Great Western Divide and many other parts of the high Sierra, the principal reason being that its granitic rocks have a fairly regular joint structure. In many alpine regions where avalanches are active in winter, snow chutes are only imperfectly developed or entirely absent, because the rock structure is too irregular.

That the snow chutes in the sides of Mount Whitney were carved chiefly during the Ice Age, while the canyons were being glaciated, is evident from the fact that they end invariably at or close to the "ice line," which marks the upper limit of glacial corrasion on the canyon walls. Avalanches have occurred, of course, through all of postglacial time and are active in winter even now, but all of this postglacial avalanching has added but little to the depth of the chutes,

Milestone Basin with Mount Whitney in the distance. By Walter L. Huber

as is demonstrated by the small size of the rock piles that lie beneath them. These rock piles obviously contain but a small fraction of the total amount of material that has been carved out of the deep chutes.

The snow conditions that prevail on the summit platform of Mount Whitney, and that have prevailed there throughout all glacial times, are intimately related to the development of the snow chutes in its sides. The avalanches are composed today, and doubtless have always been composed, in large part of snow blown from the summit platform by the winter gales. Because of its simple configuration, unaccidented by ridges, pinnacles, or ravines, that platform is windswept throughout and in every direction. As a consequence the greater part of the snow that falls upon it is blown off by the winds while still in a powdery state. As westerly gales are most prevalent the bulk is flung out to eastward in great "snow banners," such as Muir described many years ago, and swirls down in the "wind shadow" of the peak; but considerable portions of it are blown also in other directions and accumulate in massive cornices at the edges of the platform. It is the breaking down of these overhanging, unstable cornices that gives rise to the avalanches.

Those who have observed Mount Whitney in winter say that its summit is never more than thinly mantled with snow. Sometimes it is even partly bare when the valleys at lower levels are smothered beneath heavy loads of snow. The same is true of all the tabular summits of the Sierra Nevada. What is more, there is good reason to believe that closely similar conditions prevailed on them during glacial times, for the climate then was not more snowy but colder. It is entirely possible, even, that those lofty summits then bore less snow than they bear today, for because of the more intense cold the winter gales were more violent, and the zone of maximum snowfall, which today lies, according to the best data available, fully 3000 to 4000 feet below the level of the main peaks, then probably lay lower still, so that the peaks rose high into regions of relatively scant precipitation.

The summit of Mount Whitney not only has escaped glaciation, but, what may seem more astonishing, it has escaped stream erosion also, during all of glacial, interglacial, and postglacial times. Not a single streamworn gully cuts its surface, nor is there any more than the merest trace of a rainwater rill. The reason is that heavy showers are rare at its high altitude. Even in midsummer the precipitation consists in large part of snow pellets—*graupel* is the technical term—and the snowdrifts waste away chiefly by direct evaporation under the intense radiant heat of the sun, as is attested by their deeply pitted surfaces.

The small amount of meltwater that issues from the snowdrifts, nevertheless, is a source of considerable destructive energy. Congealing night after night in the crevices of the rock, it loosens up the joint blocks and in the course of time splits them into smaller and smaller fragments. The results are familiar to every mountaineer who has visited any of the tabular summits of the Sierra Nevada. They are all encumbered with frost-riven and frost-heaved blocks that make progress excessively wearisome. This type of intense frost work on unglaciated surfaces at high altitudes (and in high latitudes too) has been termed *nivation,* because it is dependent upon the presence of snowfields and snowdrifts. The top of Mount Whitney, accordingly, is properly described as a nivated summit.

It is a pertinent question at what rate the process of nivation works. How fast, or rather, how slowly is it reducing Mount Whitney in height? No observational data are at hand on which a quantitative estimate may be based, but this much can be said without fear of contradiction, that the nivation process works in general far more slowly than either stream-and-rain erosion or glacial erosion. Much depends on the character of the rock. In thin-bedded or slaty rocks that break up into shingle and small flaky fragments, an auxiliary process known as *solifluction* (literally soil-flow) sets in, that operates to remove the frost-split material. It consists of a sluggish flowlike movement that is particularly active in masses of fine material permeated and lubricated with water, causing them to gravitate down slope in tonguelike bodies that push the coarser shingle up on edge. But in the granitic rocks of the Sierra Nevada, which break up for the most part into large and heavy blocks, or locally into loose sand through which water passes as through a sieve, solifluction is not effective as a transporting agent, and as a consequence the frost-split material remains largely in place. Reduction by nivation there is necessarily very slow.

It happens that the summit of Mount Whitney is composed in large part of a fine-grained, siliceous type of granite known as aplite—the kind of rock which ordinarily occurs only in narrow dikes (veins, as they are commonly but erroneously called). This rock breaks up characteristically into large angular slabs and weathers down to sand far more slowly than the coarse-grained granite roundabout. It follows that on Mount Whitney solifluction is wholly inoperative and nivation works even more slowly than on some of the other tabular peaks of the Sierra Nevada. How slowly, you ask? Perhaps as slowly as three or four feet in 250,000 years, to judge from the rate at which certain dikes of aplite whose glacial history is definitely known appear to have been reduced by weathering. As the Ice Age and all of postglacial time together aggregate in round numbers one million years, it would follow that Mount Whitney has suffered a reduction of only 12 or 16 feet since the Ice Age began. The total reduction which Mount Whitney has suffered by erosion of all kinds since it was a lowland hill, considering the climatic conditions and the vegetational cover that existed in preglacial times, probably amounts to several hundred feet.

Remains the question, how old is Mount Whitney? How many millions of years have elapsed since it was a lowland hill? Again, only a rough estimate is

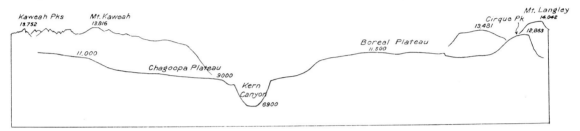

Figure 14.—Simplified east-west profile across the Upper Kern Basin showing remnants of four ancient landscapes (erosion surfaces) at different levels above the Kern Canyon. Vertical scale exaggerated. Courtesy University of California Press

possible, only an indication of the order of magnitude of the interval, based on the data that are now at hand concerning the evolution of the upper Kern Basin and the Muir Crest.

The best method of approach is by evaluating the duration of each of the successive cycles of erosion that have left their impress on the region (see Fig. 14). Without going into a full discussion of all the factors that must be considered, it may be pointed out that the Kern Canyon has been produced by stream and glacial erosion since the last great uplift of the range. It is therefore presumably about one million years old. The broad rock-benches of the Chagoopa cycle, by comparison, must have required 10 to 15 times as long an interval for their development—in round numbers, 10 to 15 million years. The still more maturely developed landscape of the Boreal Plateau cycle, then, may have required fully 20 million years, and at least another five to ten million years is to be assigned to the cycle that followed the initial uplift. The total length of time that has elapsed since the lowland stage, when Whitney Hill was only 1500 feet high, therefore appears to be of the order of 35 to 45 million years.

Reprinted from Sierra Club Bulletin, *1937, pages 1–18.*

Royal Arches,
Washington Column,
and Half Dome,
Yosemite.

By Ansel Adams

John Muir, Washington Column, Yosemite

JOHN MUIR

AND THE GLACIAL

THEORY OF YOSEMITE

JOHN MUIR'S name, it need hardly be said, will forever be associated with the Yosemite Valley which he loved so well. It will also be remembered—should be remembered—as the name of the humble nature lover who dared oppose the dictum of one of the foremost geologists of his time. The theory of that scientist, then widely accepted, was that the Yosemite had come into existence suddenly as the result of a violent convulsion of the earth, its bottom dropping out, so to speak, and leaving the sheer walls standing. Nothing but a catastrophic happening of this sort, it was believed, could have given the chasm its extraordinary shape. Yet Muir boldly advanced the unorthodox idea that the Yosemite had been gouged out primarily by a mighty glacier of the Ice Age, and that it had been elaborated little by little in the course of thousands of years.

In the controversy that ensued, Muir's theory was treated rather roughly by his opponents. Scientific controversies in those days were not conducted in the gentlemanly manner that now prevails. His views were assailed, ridiculed, and belittled as the wild fantasies of an ignorant shepherd. It seems appropriate, then, on this occasion to show where Muir's theory now stands, and to appraise its scientific worth as impartially and as dispassionately as may be, in the light of the findings of modern geologic research.

Mine was the privilege for several years, under the auspices of the United States Geological Survey, to study the complex problem of the Yosemite's mode of origin. Systematically and in detail I covered the very ground that Muir studied with so much zest. I did so, however, without the guidance of the charmingly intimate accounts of his discoveries which Muir wrote in letters to his friends, for those letters then were not yet published. My findings, therefore, were independently arrived at. Moreover, they were tested out by comparative studies in all of the other Yosemite-like valleys of the Sierra Nevada.

The results may be summed up as follows: In neither the Yosemite nor in any other valley of its type is there evidence of any dislocation of the earth's crust. In every one of these valleys, on the other hand, there is abundant proof of powerful glacial action such as Muir had recognized. To be sure, the glaciers did not reach down to the foothills, nor did they excavate the canyons in their entirety, as Muir supposed. The Ice Age, it is now clear, was preceded in the Sierra Nevada by long periods of canyon cutting by the streams in consequence of successive uplifts of the range. But let no one cite these recently determined facts to Muir's discredit, for geologic science in the sixties and seventies of last century had not advanced to the point where any man, however expert, could have detected and proved them. Whatever shortcomings may be found today in Muir's geologic interpretations, they are to be attributed primarily to the limitations of the science of his day. To one thoroughly at home in the geologic problems of the Yosemite region it is now certain, upon reading Muir's letters and other writings, that he was more intimately familiar with the facts on the ground and was more nearly right in their interpretation, than any professional geologist of his time.*

On this centennial of his birth, then, it will be a source of satisfaction to his friends and admirers to learn that, far from being in error, Muir was probably as nearly right in his glacial theory of the Yosemite as any scientist in the early seventies could have been.

Written for a broadcast, April 17, 1938. Reprinted from Sierra Club Bulletin, *1938, pages 9–10.*

* See especially, *John Muir's Studies in the Sierra.* The Sierra Club, San Francisco, 1960. 142 pages. Introduction by William E. Colby; Foreword by John P. Buwalda.

APPENDIX

Era	Period or System	Epoch or Series	Approx. no. of million years ago.[1]	Approx. length in millions of years.[1]
Cenozoic	Quaternary	Recent Pleistocene	0–1	1
	Tertiary	Pliocene	1–12	11
		Miocene	12–28	16
		Oligocene	28–40	12
		Eocene Paleocene	40–60	20
Mesozoic	Cretaceous		60–130	70
	Jurassic		130–155	25
	Triassic		155–185	30
Paleozoic	Permian		185–210	25
	Pennsylvanian (Upper Carboniferous)		210–235 [2]	25
	Mississippian (Lower Carboniferous)		235–265 [2]	30
	Devonian		265–320	55
	Silurian		320–360	40
	Ordovician		360–440	80
	Cambrian		440–520	80
Proterozoic	Pre-Cambrian		520–2100+	1600+

[1] Report of the National Research Council, Committee on the Measurement of Geologic Time, 1949–50.
[2] Estimate of J. P. Marble, Chairman of Committee on Measurement of Geologic Time, March 17, 1954.

SOME OTHER PUBLICATIONS ON THE SIERRA NEVADA
BY FRANÇOIS E. MATTHES

Superintendent of Documents, Government Printing Office, Washington 25, D.C.:

The Geologic History of Yosemite Valley. Professional Paper 160, U. S. Geological Survey, 1930.

Reconnaissance of the geomorphology and glacial geology of the San Joaquin Basin, Sierra Nevada, California. Professional Paper 329, U. S. Geological Survey, 1960.*

Glacial reconnaissance of Sequoia National Park, California. (To be published by the U. S. Geological Survey.)*

The University of California Press, Berkeley 4, California:

Sequoia National Park: a geological album. 1950.*

The Incomparable Valley: a geologic interpretation of the Yosemite. 1950.*

* Posthumous works, edited by Fritiof Fryxell.

THE END PAPER is a portion of a map of Yosemite Valley. The topography is by François Matthes and stands as one of the most beautiful topographic maps ever published. Matthes urged for many years that the United States Geological Survey should publish shaded topographic maps and left his own version of shading with the Survey upon his retirement. The portion herewith is an approximation of what he had hoped for and is reproduced in one color from the U.S.G.S. sheet, which is in five colors.

Source: U.S. Geological Survey, Map of Yosemite Valley, Yosemite National Park, California, surveyed in 1905–1906 in coöperation with the State of California and partly revised in 1934 and 1946. The shading was added in 1946, and the source sheet is one that was reprinted in 1949 with corrections. The scale is 1:24,000 (1 inch equals 2,000 feet) and North is up.